CHRISTMAS CROSSWORDS FOR KIDS

OVER 150 PUZZLES!

Buster Books

First published in Great Britain in 2020 by Buster Books,
an imprint of Michael O'Mara Books Limited,
9 Lion Yard, Tremadoc Road, London SW4 7NQ

 www.mombooks.com/buster   Buster Books   @BusterBooks    @buster_books

The material in this book previously appeared in
The Kids' Book of Christmas Crosswords

Puzzles designed and typeset by Sarah Khan

Illustrations by John Bigwood
With additional material adapted from www.shutterstock.com

Layout designed by Derrian Bradder and Janene Spencer
Cover designed by Angie Allison

A CIP catalogue record for this book is available from the British Library.

ISBN: 978-1-78055-742-7

3 5 7 9 10 8 6 4 2

Printed and bound in October 2021 by CPI Group (UK) Ltd,
108 Beddington Lane, Croydon, CR0 4YY, United Kingdom.

MIX
Paper from
responsible sources
FSC® C020471

Contents

Crossword Crazy

Crosswords are the most popular printed puzzles of all time. This book contains over 150 of them. Some of the clues will be Christmas-themed, others will be general knowledge.

The Rules Of Crosswords

The rules of crosswords are very simple: just find the solution word described by each numbered across or down clue and then write it into the corresponding squares in the grid.

Sometimes, you'll be able to think of more than one answer to a clue. When this happens, wait until you work out some of the words that cross over that one in the grid, then use these letters to help you choose the correct solution.

Each clue has a number in brackets at the end, like this: (5). This shows you how many letters are in the word you are trying to guess and matches the number of empty squares in the grid. You might see two numbers, like this: (3, 3). This means that there are two words to place, each of the given length, such as 'one day'. Don't leave a space between the words in the grid, though – write one letter in each square.

If you see a ';' in a clue, it means the clue is made up of different parts which will help you guess the solution. For example, the clue: 'Opposite of front; rear of your body (4)' provides two clues for 'back'.

You might see '(inits)' after a clue. This means the answer is made up of the initial (first) letters of each word of the solution, for example 'BTW' for 'by the way'. You will also sometimes see '(abbr)' after a clue. This means that the solution is an abbreviated (shortened) form of a word, for example 'Dec' for 'December'.

The puzzles in this book start off easy and then get tougher as the book progresses. There are four separate difficulty levels – Beginner, Intermediate, Advanced and Ace Puzzler – which are shown at the top or the side of each page. You can also time yourself. There's space to fill in exactly how long it has taken you to solve each puzzle.

If you get stuck and simply can't answer the clue then just ask a friend or family member to help you. If they can't help you either then don't despair – all the answers are at the back of the book.

Good luck, and have fun!

Level One:
Beginners

Puzzle 1

Across
1 Opposite of right (5)
3 Buzzing insect (3)
5 These jingle on Santa's sleigh (5)

Down
2 Santa delivers these (5)
4 The day before Christmas is called Christmas ___ (3)

Time ....

Puzzle 2

Across

1 You do this with Christmas cookies in the oven (4)

2 Glide across snow with a long strip of wood or plastic strapped to each foot (3)

4 Plant with prickly leaves and red berries that appear in winter (5)

Down

1 Christians celebrate the ___ of Jesus (5)

3 Climbing plant whose leaves are often used in Christmas wreaths (3)

Time ....

Puzzle 3

Across

1 Rudolph the reindeer has a red one of these (4)
3 Wear one on each hand to keep warm in winter (5)
4 To make brown and crispy by heating (5)

Down

1 Opposite of day; period when Santa delivers presents (5)
2 Santa's helpers (5)

Time ....

BEGINNERS

Puzzle 4

Across

1 Christmas trees are often this type of tree (3)
3 Concentrate hard on something (5)
4 Colour of Santa's suit (3)

Down

1 Ingredient in baking; plain or self raising (5)
2 Circular; shape of a Christmas wreath (5)

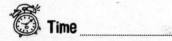

Time ....

Puzzle 5

Across
1 Stars shine brightly in the ___ (3)
5 Canes made of this are traditional Christmas sweets (5)
6 You do this when you want to know the answer to something (3)

Down
2 According to the Bible, who brought the baby Jesus gold, frankincense and myrrh (5)
3 Frozen water (3)
4 Place to exercise; adults join this as a popular New Year's resolution (3)

Time ....

Puzzle 6

Across
1 Next to (2)
2 Person in charge of playing the songs at a Christmas party (2)
4 Large musical instrument, often found in a church (5)

Down
1 Santa wears these on his feet (5)
3 This man was swallowed by a whale in the Bible (5)

Time ....

Puzzle 7

Across

1 Cover a gift (4)
4 Figure often placed on top of a Christmas tree (5)
5 Man dressed as a woman in a pantomime (4)

Down

2 North ___ , where Santa lives (4)
3 You can write in and post this at Christmas (4)

Time ....

Puzzle 8

Across
1 Soft adhesive (5)
4 Chocolate yule ___ , often eaten at Christmas (3)
5 You do this to ribbon to make a bow (3)

Down
1 Gathering to celebrate an occasion (5)
2 Shops usually have these after Christmas (5)
3 Traditional Christmas drink is made with these (4)

 **Time** ....

Puzzle 9

Across
1 Christmas song (5)
4 Throw (5)
5 Visitor in your home (5)

Down
2 Every (3)
3 Shines out of a candle (5)
4 Dried fruit; an ingredient used in Christmas pudding (3)

Time ....

Puzzle 10

Across

2 Watch in secret (3)
5 Fragrance; popular Christmas gift for men (7)
6 Boxing Day is the day ___ Christmas (5)

Down

1 Vegetable traditionally eaten at Christmas (6)
3 Opposite of come (2)
4 Christmas lights are turned this way to shine (2)

Time ....

Puzzle 11

Across
1 Feeling happy; in the Christmas spirit (5)
4 Big meal (5)
6 Opposite of from (2)

Down
2 Drama set to classical music (5)
3 Santa looks at this to see who has been naughty or nice (4)
5 Something to play with (3)

Time ....

Puzzle 12

Across

1 Female fox; one of Santa's reindeers (5)

3 Stars do this in the night sky (5)

4 You can decorate one of these for Christmas (4)

Down

1 Go to see family or friends (5)

2 French word for Christmas (4)

 Time ....

Puzzle 13

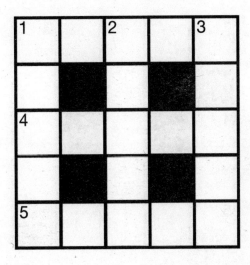

Across
1 New Year's Day is on the ___ of January (5)
4 Had possession of (5)
5 Delicious (5)

Down
1 Layer of ice (5)
2 There are five gold ones of these in "The Twelve Days of Christmas" (5)
3 Toy bear; popular Christmas gift for a child (5)

Time ....

Puzzle 14

Across

1 Second meal of the day; often the main Christmas meal (5)

5 ___ Christmas; a common festive greeting (5)

Down

2 It's now or ___ (5)

3 ___ New Year; a popular New Year's greeting (5)

4 Type of pork; often eaten at Christmas particularly in Australia and Sweden (3)

Time ....

Puzzle 15

Across

4 Two people often play this animal in a pantomime (5)
5 Mary Poppins' job (5)

Down

1 What you do to someone who gives you a gift (5)
2 Hot chocolate and punch are both a type of this (5)
3 Extremely (4)

Puzzle 16

Across

1 Type of hat (3)
4 Roman god of love; name of one of Santa's reindeer (5)
5 Fool's Day is celebrated on the first of this month (5)

Down

1 Hot drink; often left out for Santa on Christmas Eve (5)
2 Patterned rolls of this are used to wrap Christmas presents (5)
3 Award given for an achievement (5)

 Time ....

Puzzle 17

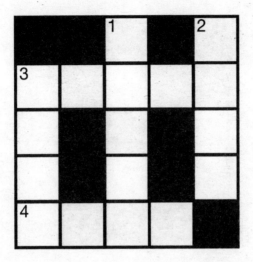

Across

3 Glide across ice (5)
4 In the Bible the three kings that visited the baby Jesus are ___ men (4)

Down

1 Different types of these are often played after Christmas lunch (5)
2 A partridge is in this tree in "The Twelve Days of Christmas" (4)
3 Often falls in winter when it is very cold outside (4)

Time ....

Puzzle 18

Across
2 What you do to the doors on an advent calendar (4)
4 Opposite of off (2)
5 Once more (5)

Down
1 A carol is a ___ about Christmas (4)
3 The number of Santa's reindeers including Rudolph (4)
4 Type of paddle used to row a rowing boat (3)

 Time ....

Puzzle 19

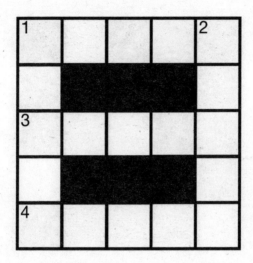

Across

1 You can keep your Christmas photos in one of these books (5)
3 Yellow citrus fruit (5)
4 Colour of Santa's beard and snow (5)

Down

1 Give permission (5)
2 Type of sweet pie traditionally eaten at Christmas (5)

Time ....

Puzzle 20

Across

2 Hello, informally (2)
3 Mother of Jesus (4)
4 Found dancing with eight others in "The Twelve Days of Christmas" (4)

Down

1 Type of twinkling light often used as Christmas decorations (5)
2 Used to have (3)
3 Mother, informally (2)

 Time ....

Puzzle 21

Across

1 Sound made when a Christmas cracker is pulled (4)
4 Place to ice skate (4)
5 Turkey and geese are this type of animal (4)

Down

2 Not wearing any clothes (5)
3 Jesus didn't have one of these for a bed in "Away in a Manger" (4)

Time ....

BEGINNERS

Puzzle 22

Across

1 Children can do this on Santa's knee when they visit his grotto (3)

3 Place to lodge (3)

4 The jokes in Christmas crackers try to make you do this (5)

Down

1 In the Bible, Jesus was Mary's ___ (3)

2 Eating too many candy canes would be bad for this part of your mouth (5)

3 Unwell; how you might feel if you overeat at Christmas (3)

 Time ....

Puzzle 23

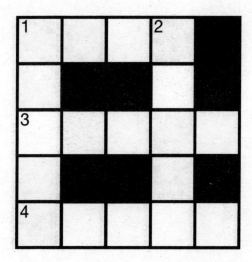

Across

1 What you might accidentally do if you walk on an icy path (4)
3 Sugary layer covering a cake or topping a biscuit (5)
4 Opposite of loose (5)

Down

1 ___ Nicholas; another name for Santa (5)
2 Fruity drink often served at parties (5)

Time ....

Puzzle 24

Across

2 You might wear woollen clothes in winter to keep you feeling this (4)

4 You can fry food in this (3)

5 "___ the Halls" is a Christmas carol (4)

Down

1 Church bells swing to and ___ to make a ringing sound (3)

2 Thin rod used by fairies to help them do magic (4)

3 Source of calcium (4)

 Time ....

Puzzle 25

Across
2 Put your arms around someone (3)
5 You might go out for one of these after Christmas lunch (4)

Down
1 Timid; not confident around others (3)
3 If you are happy or pleased about something (4)
4 People who like crafting often ___ their own Christmas decorations (4)

Time ....

Puzzle 26

Across

1 You can wear this around your neck to keep it warm (5)

3 Animal that meows (3)

5 Traditional to do this under the mistletoe (4)

Down

1 Santa carries his gifts around in this kind of bag (4)

2 Performs in a play or movie (4)

4 Direct; point (3)

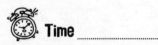

Time ....

Puzzle 27

Across
1 Spider makes this (3)
4 Opposite of in (3)
5 In the Bible, the wise men followed this to find the baby Jesus (4)

Down
1 Candles are made of this (3)
2 Sturdy item of footwear (5)
3 Tale told for entertainment (5)

Time ....

BEGINNERS

Puzzle 28

Across

1 You do this to a Christmas cracker (4)
3 Finished; done with (4)
4 When something is burned it turns to this (3)

Down

1 You can pose for one of these with Santa in his grotto (5)
2 These are leaping in "The Twelve Days of Christmas" (5)

 Time ....

Puzzle 29

Across

1 The Grinch had a pet one of these (3)
3 The ___ Plum Fairy is a character in "The Nutcracker" ballet (5)
4 Grains used to make porridge (4)

Down

1 You might dance to this kind of music at a party (5)
2 Elves have pointed ___ on either side of their heads (4)

Time

Puzzle 30

Across

3 You might get a ___ of coal in your Christmas stocking if you have been naughty (4)

4 Santa only gives gifts to children who have been this during the year (4)

Down

1 How you would describe someone who has lived a long time (3)

2 Type of ingredient used to flavour food (5)

4 Opposite of yes (2)

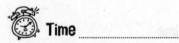

Time ....

Puzzle 31

Across
1 Piece of holly (5)
3 Opposite of beginning (3)
4 Piece of furniture around which people gather to eat meals (5)

Down
1 Small sugary treat (5)
2 Snow ___ ; ornament that is shaken to create the appearance of snowfall inside (5)

Time ....

BEGINNERS

Puzzle 32

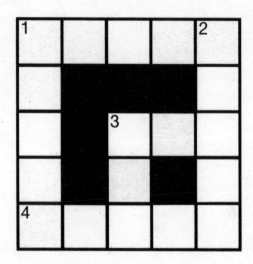

Across

1 Small morsel of bread or cake (5)
3 Hot drink made from leaves (3)
4 Very fast (5)

Down

1 Group of singers that perform in public, often in a church (5)
2 Santa has a long white ___ growing from his chin (5)
3 Position of star or angel on a Christmas tree (3)

 Time ....

Puzzle 33

Across

2 "___ the Herald Angels Sing" (4)

4 Drink something by taking small mouthfuls (3)

5 One of the gifts brought by the wise men to baby Jesus in the Bible (4)

Down

1 ___ Claus, Santa's wife (3)

2 What you do to stockings and mistletoe at Christmas time (4)

3 Considerate; helpful (4)

Time ....

BEGINNERS

Puzzle 34

Across

1 Put on clothes (5)
4 Christmas crackers usually contain a paper one of these (5)

Down

1 You might do this to music at a party (5)
2 Take pleasure in something (5)
3 Steam bath; traditional to have one of these on Christmas Day in Finland (5)

 Time ....

Puzzle 35

Across

2 Plays are often performed on one of these (5)
4 Small seed in a fruit (3)
6 Celebrated at midnight on Christmas Eve in churches around the world (4)

Down

1 Christmas celebrates the birth of this person (5)
3 ___ the tree; decorate (4)
5 Father in the USA (2)

Time ....

Puzzle 36

Across

3 Put ice cream in one (4)
4 Informal word for a party; to make something happen (2)
5 Elves wear jingling, pointed shoes on these parts of their bodies (4)

Down

1 Eat quickly (5)
2 "___ in Royal David's City" (4)

Time ....

Level Two:

Intermediates

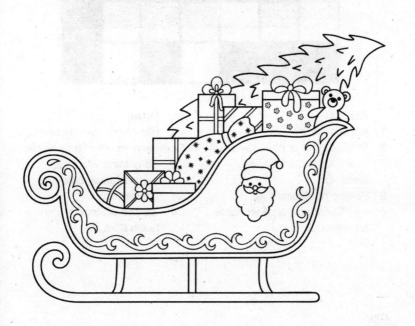

Puzzle 37

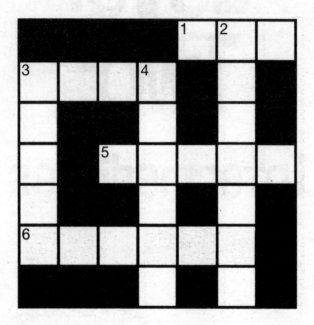

Across

1 Horses eat this (3)
3 Strip of cloth or ribbon worn over your shoulder and waist (4)
5 Feeling of coldness (5)
6 ___ Christmas; another name for Santa (6)

Down

2 Reindeers have these growing out of their heads (7)
3 Something you might do to a turkey before cooking it (5)
4 Santa's distinctive laugh (2, 2, 2)

 Time ....

Puzzle 38

Across

1 Found on a strip of paper inside a Christmas cracker (4)
4 Thin strips of pasta (7)
7 Sadness (3)
8 Children do this to see if they can hear Santa's sleigh bells (6)
9 Scrooge was visited by three of these in Dickens' "A Christmas Carol" (6)

Down

1 Sound made by sleigh bells (6)
2 Santa ___ whether you have been naughty or nice (5)
3 Person who invites people for a meal or party (4)
5 Small round mark or spot (3)
6 Vegetable often found in traditional Welsh recipes (5)

Time ....

Puzzle 39

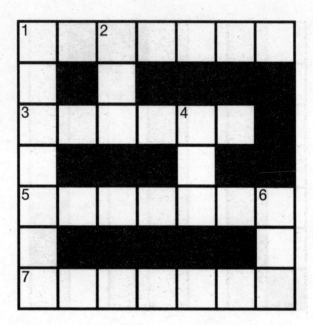

Across

1 Salty or sweet snack (7)
3 One of Santa's reindeer who likes to party (6)
5 The host does this to the people they want to come to their gathering (7)
7 Wreath of flowers; leaves or other material worn or hung up for decoration (7)

Down

1 Type of Christmas dessert that is made with figs or plums (7)
2 Tool used for writing with ink (3)
4 People tend do a lot of this at Christmas, particularly around the dining table (3)
6 Unhappy (3)

 Time ....

Puzzle 40

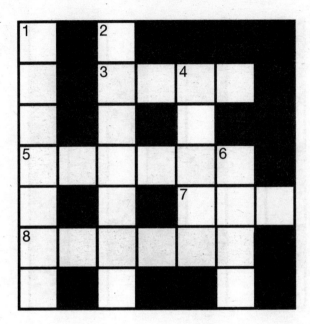

Across

3 Unattractive (4)
5 Clean until shiny (6)
7 Do this with your eyes (3)
8 Long narrow strip of fabric; used for tying something or for decoration (6)

Down

1 Sweaters; patterned ones are often worn at Christmas (7)
2 Song sung to put a child to sleep (7)
4 Rope with a loop at one end; used by cowboys (5)
6 Three French varieties of this bird are in "The Twelve Days of Christmas" (4)

Time ....

INTERMEDIATES

Puzzle 41

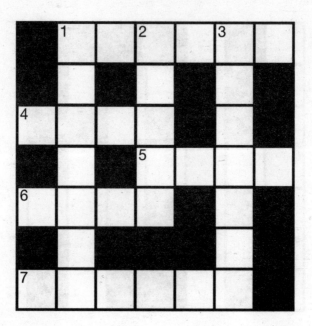

Across

1 To be carried or posted (6)
4 Santa's elves and reindeer ___ him deliver gifts (4)
5 White fat used in cooking (4)
6 Refuse to accept or admit something (4)
7 Steady; where horses sleep (6)

Down

1 Gift (7)
2 Answer in response to something (5)
3 Hug (7)

 Time ....

Puzzle 42

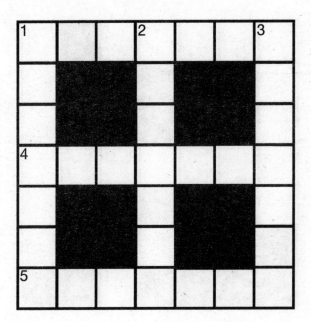

Across

1 These are placed in an Advent wreath and lit weekly during the month leading up to Christmas (7)

4 More frothy (7)

5 Popular birds eaten for Christmas lunch (7)

Down

1 "Tidings of ___ and joy" (7)

2 Scandinavian country famous for its pastries and butter cookies (7)

3 "A Christmas Carol" and "The Little Match Girl" are both ___ set at Christmas time (7)

Time _____

INTERMEDIATES

Puzzle 43

Across

1 Holy book for Christians (5)
4 Quick look; children sometimes try to stay up on Christmas Eve to get a ___ of Santa (7)
7 The flat area between the waist and the knees of a seated person (3)
8 Circular arrangement of leaves, berries and ornaments; used as a decoration (6)

Down

1 Large tree branch (5)
2 More crowded or active; shops tend to be this in the run up to Christmas (6)
3 Mary's husband in the Nativity story (6)
5 Watch this on stage (4)
6 "Humpty Dumpty ___ on a wall" (3)

 Time ....

Puzzle 44

Across

1 Acted in a specified way; well ___ (7)

4 Fairy tale monster that eats people (4)

6 Gift label (3)

8 Santa's mode of transport on Christmas Eve (6)

9 Negative; is ___ (3)

Down

2 Word said at the end of a prayer or hymn that means "so be it" (4)

3 Great pleasure (7)

5 Cinderella's party shoes were made of this (5)

6 In "The Wizard of Oz", Dorothy's heartless friend is made of this (3)

7 Before the present; earlier (3)

Time ....

INTERMEDIATES

Puzzle 45

Across

2 The collar and cuffs of Santa's cloak are made from this hairy material (3)
5 Drank noisily (7)
6 When you knead dough you fold and ___ it (7)
7 King Wenceslas is described as this (4)
8 Fizzy water often mixed with other drinks (4)

Down

1 Immense happiness and excitement (7)
2 Companions (7)
3 Opposite of down (2)
4 Saved (7)

 Time ....

Puzzle 46

Across

1 ___ Frost; mythical character who represents winter (4)
4 Piece of material spread over a table especially during meals (5)
5 Similar to a brownie, but made with vanilla instead of chocolate (7)
6 Circular toy attached to a string that can move up and down (2, 2)

Down

1 Long trip (7)
2 @ (2)
3 Giving money or time to people who are in need (7)
4 Dark mineral used as fuel for fires (4)
5 Cube often made of cardboard which can be used as packaging (3)

Time ....

Puzzle 47

Across

1 No war or hostility (5)
4 Give to a charity or good cause (6)
5 "While Shepherds Watched Their ___" (6)
6 One of the gifts given by the three wise men to baby Jesus in the Bible (5)

Down

1 Ride a bicycle (5)
2 Paper cylinder that makes a small bang and releases a gift when pulled apart (7)
3 Piece of furniture for sleeping (3)
5 Common New Year's resolution is to become this by exercising more (3)

 Time ....

INTERMEDIATES

Puzzle 48

Across

1 Make something holy (5)
3 Set the table (3)
5 Way of serving potatoes that involves breaking them up (6)
7 Disc with a film or TV show on it (inits) (3)
8 Charles ___ ; author (7)

Down

2 Vehicle used for travelling over snow that has long strips of metal or wood instead of wheels (4)
4 The four weeks leading up to Christmas (6)
5 These are "a-milking" in "The Twelve Days of Christmas" (5)
6 Piece of cake or pie (5)

Time ....

Puzzle 49

Across

2 "We ___ You a Merry Christmas" (4)
4 Hanging decoration can be made by linking coloured paper loops to form this (5)
5 Without feeling; your fingers and toes can become this in very cold weather (4)
6 Type of curry invented in Britain (5)
7 Engrave; carve (4)
8 Animal with antlers (4)

Down

1 Less expensive (7)
2 Coldest season of the year (6)
3 Group of people native to the Arctic regions of Greenland, Canada and Alaska (5)

Time ....

Puzzle 50

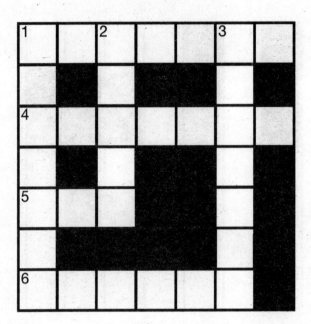

Across

1 Greeting to a guest (7)
4 Without pausing for a break (7)
5 Possess (3)
6 "___ night, holy night" (6)

Down

1 Parts of shops where Christmas displays are put up to attract passers-by (7)
2 High quality tablecloths and napkins are usually made from this kind of material (5)
3 Illuminated by light coming from the moon (7)

Time ....

Puzzle 51

Across

2 Logs do this in a fire (4)
3 Small crawling insect that lives in a colony (3)
5 Figure made out of snow (7)
7 "___ We Come A-Carolling" (4)
8 Name of one of Santa's reindeers who moves with high, springy steps (7)

Down

1 Tall machine used for lifting heavy objects (5)
2 Christmas Day is the day ___ Christmas Eve and Boxing Day (7)
4 Neither here ___ there (3)
5 Place to buy Christmas presents (4)
6 Close to (4)

 Time ....

Puzzle 52

Across

2 Fill a bag with things you need to travel (4)

4 The villain in "Jack and the Beanstalk" (5)

7 Tangle of hair (3)

8 Coloured glass in a church window (7)

Down

1 Shining; brilliant (6)

3 Tool for making shapes from dough (6)

5 "See ___ the Winter's Snow" (4)

6 Grandma, informally (3)

Time ....

Puzzle 53

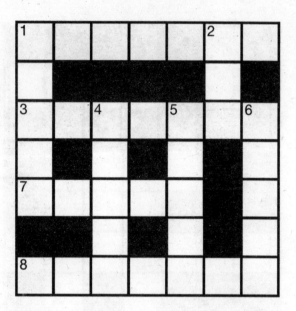

Across

1 The part of a house that Santa comes down when delivering gifts (7)

3 Hanging pieces of ice formed when dripping water freezes (7)

7 Planned party (5)

8 Spend a lot of money (7)

Down

1 Make a ringing sound (5)

2 Lump of coal can be used for this part of a snowman's face (3)

4 Perfectly suited (5)

5 At some time in the future (5)

6 Give someone food or drink (5)

 Time ....

Puzzle 54

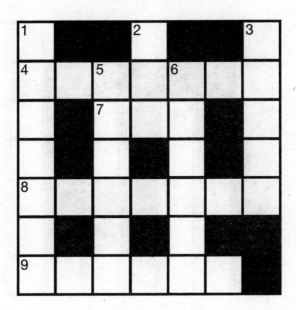

Across

4 Rose-shaped ornament that is given as a prize for an achievement (7)

7 Large Australian bird that can't fly but can run very fast (3)

8 Put mail in here (7)

9 Christmas trees are decorated with this shiny material (6)

Down

1 Brass wind instrument (7)

2 Precious or semi-precious stone (3)

3 Take it easy (5)

5 Period of the year (6)

6 Fall (6)

Time ....

INTERMEDIATES

Puzzle 55

Across

1 Send this to Santa in the post (6)
5 Happy; pleased (4)
6 Los Angeles (inits) (2)
7 Name of a male cat or turkey (3)
8 Feeling given out by a source of heat (6)

Down

2 Attached; how a knot or bow is formed (4)
3 Name of Santa's reindeer that has a shiny nose (7)
4 South American long-necked animal with soft, woolly fur (5)
5 Warm steady light (4)

 Time ....

Puzzle 56

Across

1 Type of pine tree often used as a Christmas tree (6)
3 Thin, flat bread that can be separated into two layers to form a pocket (4)
5 Dessert that is eaten during celebrations such as Christmas and birthdays (4)
6 Relax (4)
7 Type of band made up of musicians mainly playing wind instruments (5)

Down

1 What you might do at the camera when someone is taking your picture (5)
2 American biscuits; children leave these out for Santa on Christmas Eve in the USA (7)
4 Person who plays a role performing in a play, movie or on television (5)
6 Tear; pull apart (3)

Time ....

INTERMEDIATES

Puzzle 57

Across

1 Small amounts of food eaten between meals (6)
4 Building; made out of gingerbread as a traditional Christmas decoration (5)
5 Say yes to an invitation (6)
7 Pen or enclosure for a pig (3)

Down

2 Christian place of worship (6)
3 Shepherds look after these animals (5)
4 Vital organ (5)
6 Sharp pull; what you give to open a Christmas cracker (3)

 Time ....

Puzzle 58

Across

1 Teddy is usually a toy one of these animals (4)
4 Ask desperately (3)
5 Baby Jesus lay in this in the Bible (6)
6 Not polite (4)
7 Gloves that have one part for your thumb and one for your other fingers (7)

Down

1 Under (7)
2 Birds lay one of these (3)
3 Not widely available (4)
4 Not good (3)
5 Carols are Christmas poems set to ___ (5)

Time ....

INTERMEDIATES

Puzzle 59

Across

2 Common name for influenza (3)
3 Sixty seconds (6)
8 One of Santa's reindeers that moves quickly from place to place (6)
9 Post (4)

Down

1 Last name (7)
2 The giant from "Jack and the Beanstalk" shouts "Fee, Fi, Fo, ___" (3)
4 Identification (abbr) (2)
5 The United States of America (inits) (3)
6 Slim (4)
7 Snake-like fish; often eaten on Christmas Eve in Italy (3)

 Time ....

Puzzle 60

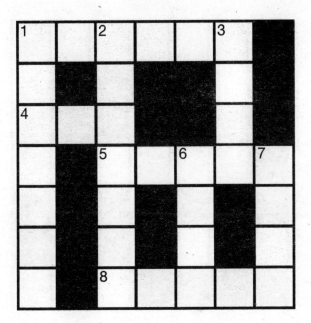

Across

1 Mary rode to Bethlehem on this animal in the Bible (6)
4 Tell an untruth (3)
5 Like raisins and prunes (5)
8 There are seven of these birds swimming in "The Twelve Days of Christmas" (5)

Down

1 Hand over a parcel (7)
2 Pine trees have these instead of broad leaves (7)
3 Old-fashioned word for Christmas (4)
6 Suggestion for doing something (4)
7 There are seven of these between Christmas and New Year (4)

Time ....

Puzzle 61

Across

1 Put someone under a spell (7)
5 Round Christmas ornament that is usually hung on a Christmas tree (6)
7 Rind of an orange or lemon (4)
8 Knot tied with two loops and two loose ends used as a decoration or to fasten shoelaces (3)

Down

2 Take a small bite (6)
3 Story (4)
4 How you feel after you have eaten enough (4)
6 Board game played by rolling dice and moving counters (4)

 Time ....

Puzzle 62

Across

2 The ladies are doing this in "The Twelve Days of Christmas" (7)
5 Unfasten; loosen (4)
6 Food limitation (4)
7 Glowing circle above an angel's head (4)

Down

1 The name of the angel who told Mary that she was going to have baby Jesus in the Bible (7)
3 Walking support (6)
4 Santa's cave (6)

Time ....

Puzzle 63

Across

1 Useful (7)
4 Liked a lot (5)
6 Evening meals (7)
8 Opposite of old (5)

Down

1 Time off school or work (7)
2 Soft creamy sweet (5)
3 Santa ___ at the North Pole (5)
5 Ice cream can be sold from this kind of vehicle (3)
7 Female member of a religious group; lives in a convent (3)

 **Time** ....

Puzzle 64

Across

1 Unwanted junk email (4)

5 Type of lizard found in hot countries (5)

7 Green gemstone (7)

8 Place where people gather to buy and sell things from stalls (6)

Down

2 Baked sweet or savoury dish; often topped with a pastry crust (3)

3 Give money to pay for something you want (5)

4 Long journey of discovery (6)

5 Produce or reflect; bright light (5)

6 Shout of praise or encouragement (5)

Time ....

Puzzle 65

Across

3 Join to something to increase its size or number (3)

5 Large number of people gathered together (5)

6 Remove the covering from a gift (6)

7 Number of geese in "The Twelve Days of Christmas" (3)

8 What a person does to make a jumper or scarf out of wool (5)

Down

1 Playing card; can be the highest or lowest card in a game (3)

2 "O Little ___ of Bethlehem" (4)

3 The details of the location of a place; write this on an envelope or parcel (7)

4 Far down (4)

6 Fairy tales often start "Once ___ a time" (4)

 Time ....

Puzzle 66

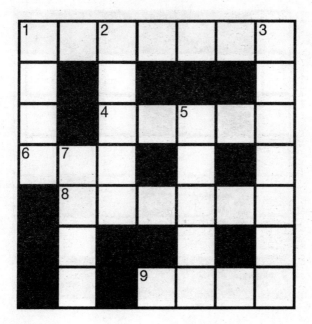

Across

1 Vegetables left out for Santa's reindeer on Christmas Eve; used as noses for snowmen (7)

4 Hawaiian greeting (5)

6 Opposite of no (3)

8 To act violently against someone or something (6)

9 Bamboo stem (4)

Down

1 Comfortable and warm (4)

2 Do this to a turkey to cook it for Christmas lunch (5)

3 Glitter with lots of points of light (7)

5 Former US president (5)

7 Opposite of difficult (4)

Time ....

INTERMEDIATES

Puzzle 67

Across

2 Large deep spoon with a long handle (5)

6 Very impressive (7)

7 Mysterious or supernatural power; Santa uses this to make his reindeer fly (5)

Down

1 What someone says when they ask for something politely (6)

3 Series of thoughts and events that happen in someone's mind while they sleep (5)

4 As much as is necessary (6)

5 Formal talk given to an audience (6)

 Time ....

Puzzle 68

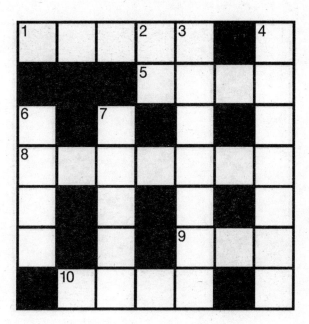

Across

1 Ice cream utensil (5)
5 Artificial (4)
8 Printed on the windows of Advent calendars (7)
9 Number of lords leaping in "The Twelve Days of Christmas" (3)
10 Dirty or untidy state (4)

Down

2 Used to indicate possession; one ___ us (2)
3 Mother and father (7)
4 ___ greetings; a common phrase written on Christmas cards (7)
6 Popular card game (4)
7 To entertain or make someone laugh (5)

Time ....

INTERMEDIATES

Puzzle 69

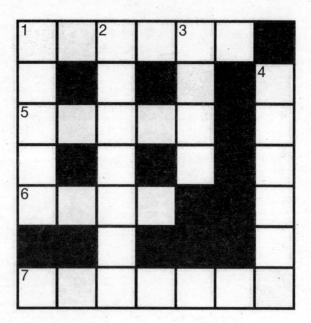

Across

1 Generous and affectionate (6)
5 Grown up (5)
6 Roald ___ ; famous children's author (4)
7 Scent; fragrance (7)

Down

1 Magnificent; posh (5)
2 Card or piece of paper that can be used instead of money to pay for something (7)
3 Savoury snacks (4)
4 Problem designed to test knowledge (6)

 Time ....

Puzzle 70

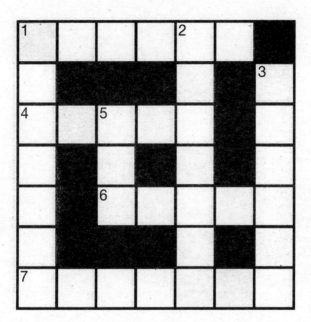

Across

1 Photograph someone has taken of themselves (6)

4 Stand in line (5)

6 Press and stretch a mixture for making dough (5)

7 Settle or move into a warm, comfortable position (7)

Down

1 Small shiny discs sewn on to clothing for decoration (7)

2 Large mass of ice that floats in the sea (7)

3 Vehicle or toy used to slide downhill on ice or snow (6)

5 Large North American deer with big antlers (3)

Time ....

Puzzle 71

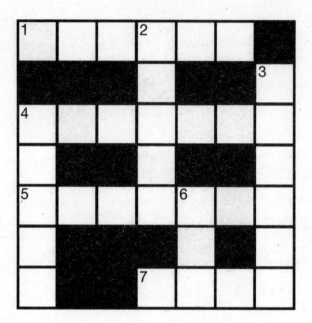

Across

1 Sherlock ___ is a fictional detective (6)
4 The inside of a pie (7)
5 The sound someone makes when they sneeze (7)
7 "Oh what fun ___ ___ to ride on a one-horse open sleigh" (2, 2)

Down

2 Ice ___ when temperature rises (5)
3 Dome-shaped houses built from blocks of solid snow (6)
4 Light that is produced when something is burnt (5)
6 Wear on your head (3)

 Time ....

Puzzle 72

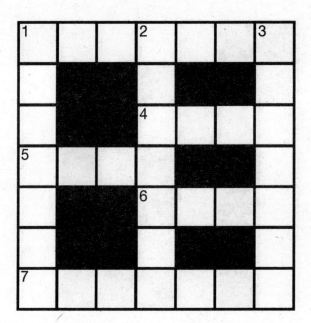

Across

1 Steep slope which turns up at the end (3, 4)
4 You change this while riding a bike if you are going up or downhill (4)
5 Call on the telephone (4)
6 Decorated cake (4)
7 Close-fitting protective glasses (7)

Down

1 Giving someone a part of something that is yours (7)
2 Running at a steady, gentle pace for exercise; taking this up is a popular New Year's resolution (7)
3 Public processions to celebrate an event or special day (7)

Time ....

INTERMEDIATES

Puzzle 73

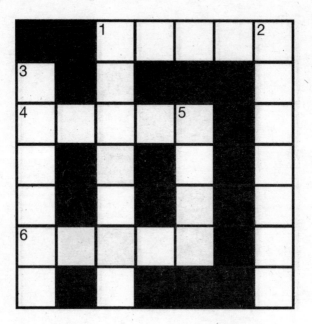

Across
1 "Rudolph the Red- ___ Reindeer" (5)
4 Settee; a covered chair for more than one person (5)
6 Frequently; regularly (5)

Down
1 Badly behaved (7)
2 Snow White's friends (7)
3 Film genre; may feature car chases and explosions (6)
5 Religious song (4)

 Time ....

Puzzle 74

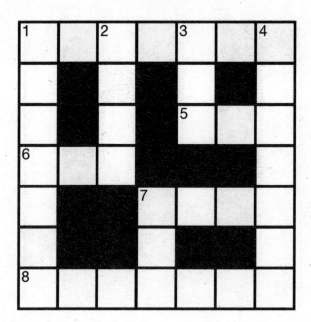

Across

1 Style of cooking that is particular to a certain place (7)
5 Short sleep (3)
6 Woodland animal's home; the place where a bear hibernates during winter (3)
7 An area or region (4)
8 Helping of food after the first one (7)

Down

1 Ashes; Cinderella's nickname (7)
2 Piece of equipment that is heated to make clothes flat (4)
3 Coloured liquid used for writing and printing (3)
4 "Polar ___"; a film and book about a boy's train journey to the North Pole (7)
7 Place where animals are kept so people can look at them (3)

Time ....

INTERMEDIATES

Puzzle 75

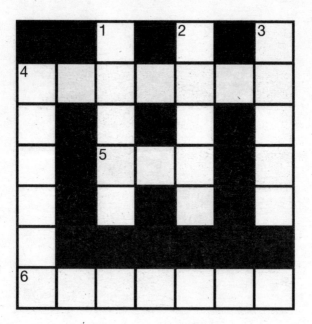

Across

4 Large formal meal for many people (7)

5 One of the five movable parts at the end of your foot (3)

6 Glisten and shine (7)

Down

1 Togetherness (5)

2 Quilt filled with feathers or fibres (5)

3 Glue together (5)

4 Purchasing (6)

 Time ....

Puzzle 76

Across

1 Piece of equipment for weighing things used especially in baking (6)
3 "All is ___, all is bright" (4)
5 Form of Japanese wrestling (4)
7 The folk-tale hero who finds a genie in a lamp (7)
8 Father, informally (3)

Down

1 Cooking utensil; used for lifting and mixing (7)
2 The flat surface of a television or computer on which images are displayed (6)
4 The way you feel at a particular time (4)
5 Unhappy (3)
6 Crazy (3)

Time ....

INTERMEDIATES

Puzzle 77

Across
1 Determined attempt (6)
5 Open pie containing a sweet or savoury filling (4)
7 Unexpected event (7)

Down
2 Outdoor event with games, rides and food stalls (7)
3 Killer whale (4)
4 Small gift to put inside a Christmas stocking (6)
6 Name; small cut (4)

Time ....

Puzzle 78

Across

2 Send in the mail (4)
3 Friend or ___ (3)
5 Something soft and shapeless (4)
6 Grandpa's wife; the name of Wendy's dog in "Peter Pan" (4)
7 On the internet (6)

Down

1 Female deer (3)
2 Vegetable used to make crisps and chips (6)
4 The number of kings that visited the baby Jesus in the Bible (5)
5 Shopping centre in the USA (4)

Time ....

Puzzle 79

Across
1 Large, usually wooden container filled with water (3, 3)
5 Type of puzzle; fit shaped pieces together to form an image (6)
6 "Mary ___ that mother mild" (3)
7 One of four corner supports, where you might hang your Christmas stocking (7)

Down
2 Place in a desert; water and plants thrive here (5)
3 Raise a glass to the health or in honour of someone (5)
4 Extinguish a candle by breathing heavily on it (4, 3)
5 Hard, usually green stone that can be carved to make ornaments (4)

Time ....

Puzzle 80

Across

3 Part of a house where Santa might land his sleigh on Christmas Eve (4)

5 Weaving machine (4)

6 Having a healthy, pink complexion (4)

8 Pleasant musical sound made by different notes sounding at the same time (7)

Down

1 Without doubt; really (5)

2 The floor of a fireplace (6)

4 Your parents and siblings (6)

7 Polite or respectful way of addressing a man (3)

Time ....

Puzzle 81

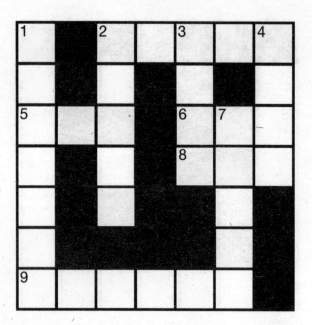

Across

2 Bird with a reddish face and breast (5)
5 Laughing out loud (inits) (3)
6 Resort that offers health and beauty treatments (3)
8 "We'll take a cup o' kindness ___" from "Auld Lang Syne" (3)
9 Covers with a smooth and glossy coating or surface (6)

Down

1 Four birds are doing this in "The Twelve Days of Christmas" (7)
2 Rest (5)
3 Working hard; fully occupied (4)
4 Clean and tidy (4)
7 When a bell rings loudly and repeatedly (5)

 Time ....

Puzzle 82

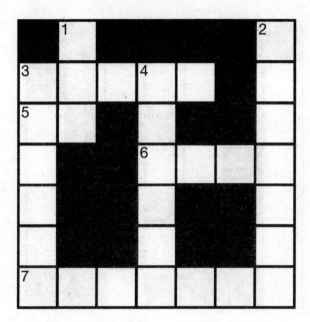

Across

3 Become infected with; you can " ___ a cold" (5)
5 Chemical symbol for americium (2)
6 Alone; without other people (4)
7 The European country in which the first Christmas markets were held (7)

Down

1 Sweet, thick spread that is made by cooking fruit with sugar (3)
2 Opposite of sweet (7)
3 Being kind and showing concern for others (6)
4 Way of behaving or a belief that is traditional to a certain place or people (6)

Time ....

INTERMEDIATES

Puzzle 83

Across

2 ___ Day; day after Christmas Day (6)

4 Special gift (5)

6 Small, silvery fish which can be pickled or salted; eaten as a special Christmas dish in many Scandinavian countries (7)

Down

1 The way out (4)

2 Purchased (6)

3 Male deer (4)

5 ___ Blyton; famous children's author (4)

 Time ....

Puzzle 84

Across

3 Keen (5)

5 "Romeo and ___" is a play by Shakespeare (6)

6 First part of the Bible, the Old Testament (inits) (2)

7 Sauce made with meat juices and flour (5)

Down

1 Eggs of various large fish; a rare and expensive food (6)

2 Feeling cheerful and ready for Christmas (7)

4 Divide using a knife (3)

5 Young kangaroo (4)

Time ....

Puzzle 85

Across

1 Opposite of go (4)
6 Something that can be eaten (6)
8 Piece of metal or plastic with an image on it that can be fastened to your clothes (5)
9 Sound a turkey makes (6)

Down

2 Small sachet with leaves inside; used to make a hot drink (6)
3 Strange, weird (3)
4 Farmyard animal (3)
5 Holly plants have red ___ (7)
7 Gamble (3)

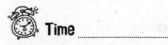 **Time** ....

Puzzle 86

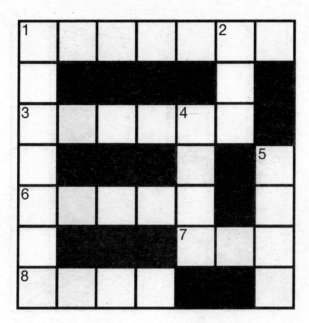

Across

1 Shy; modest (7)
3 Ask someone to join you (6)
6 Black and white striped animal (5)
7 Opposite of lose (3)
8 Short informal letter or written message (4)

Down

1 One of Santa's reindeers; "flash" in German (7)
2 Take; consume (3)
4 Ice or snow beginning to melt (4)
5 Eat dinner (4)

Time ....

INTERMEDIATES

Puzzle 87

Across
1 Friendly; sweet drink (7)
4 Perfect happiness (5)
7 Intense dislike (4)
8 Feeling of great pleasure and happiness (3)
9 Time gone by (4)

Down
2 Wise bird (3)
3 Enthusiastic and cheerful (6)
4 Newborn child (4)
5 Some French children leave these items of clothing out for Santa to fill with gifts (5)
6 Chance to speak (3)

 **Time** ....

Puzzle 88

Across

3 The shape of a person (6)
4 The outer or furthest points of something (5)
7 "We Three Kings of Orient ___" (3)
8 In England, New Year is traditionally signalled by the chiming of ___ Ben (3)

Down

1 Have the same opinion; decide something together (5)
2 "Holy infant so ___ and mild" (6)
3 Black ___ ; informal name for the day after Thanksgiving in the USA (6)
5 Joke told by a comedian (3)
6 Lay the table (3)

Time

Puzzle 89

Across
1 Desert animal that stores fat in its hump (5)
4 In need of a map (4)
5 Volcano that might erupt at any time (6)
6 Solar or lunar event; occurs when the sun or the moon become darker because light is blocked (7)

Down
1 Opposite of hot (4)
2 Play or film during which songs are performed (7)
3 Reindeer's feet (6)

 Time ....

Puzzle 90

Across

1 Thick liquid added to food to give flavour (5)
4 Items of clothing that keep your feet warm (5)
5 Piece of string that runs through the middle of a candle and burns (4)
6 Repeated decorative design (7)

Down

1 Covering of snow on the top of a mountain (7)
2 Someone who prepares food (4)
3 Someone who skims across ice (6)
4 Smell or perfume (5)

Time ....

INTERMEDIATES

Puzzle 91

Across
3 Large male pig (3)
6 There, They're and ___ (5)
7 American term for a vehicle used in the snow (4)

Down
1 Digging tools (7)
2 Bring or get together (6)
4 Kind and quiet (6)
5 Annual; every twelve months (6)

Time ....

Puzzle 92

Across

1 Older female relative (4)
2 Ice Queen in Disney's "Frozen" (4)
3 Very small; Tim Cratchit in "A Christmas Carol" (4)
4 Not mixed with anything else (4)
5 "We three kings of Orient are, bearing gifts we traverse ___" (4)
6 List of dishes available at a restaurant (4)
7 Christmas, informally (4)

Down

1 French word for cakes; usually contain layers of cream or fruit (7)

Time ....

Level Three:
Advanced

Puzzle 93

Across

2 And so on; et cetera (inits) (3)
4 Piece of equipment for cooking or heating (5)
7 The first meal of the day (9)
8 Musical about an orphan girl (5)
11 How old something is (3)

Down

1 Leg garments; hung up on Christmas Eve for Santa to leave gifts in (9)
2 Alien who wants to go home (2)
3 Curriculum vitae (inits) (2)
5 Noah's ship (3)
6 Connection point that can connect a computer to other pieces of equipment (3)
9 Not applicable (inits) (2)
10 Id est (inits) (2)

Time ....

Puzzle 94

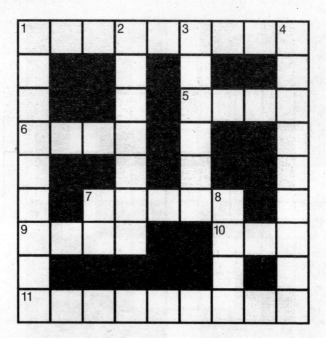

Across

1 People who look after sheep (9)

5 Happy excitement; a singing club (4)

6 "All I ___ For Christmas Is You" (4)

7 The sound a horse makes (5)

9 Jump in ice skating which can be a double or a triple (4)

10 Phrase spoken by the bride and groom (1, 2)

11 Type of tree that keeps its leaves over winter (9)

Down

1 Small, delicate arrangement of ice crystals that falls as snow (9)

2 Brittle or chewy type of bread, often shaped like a knot (7)

3 Sweet drink; traditionally drunk at Christmas (6)

4 The yellow seeds of a maize plant which are eaten as a vegetable (9)

7 North East (inits) (2)

8 Long walk, especially in the countryside (4)

 Time ....

Puzzle 95

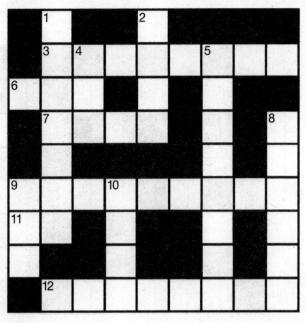

Across

3 Done with affection (8)
6 Success, come in first place (3)
7 Any occasion during the day when food is eaten (4)
9 "It's A ___ Life", Christmas movie released in 1946 (9)
11 Chemical symbol for indium (2)
12 Santa's elves make toys in this place (8)

Down

1 Mount a horse (5, 2)
2 Cash register (4)
4 Number of partridges in "The Twelve Days of Christmas" (3)
5 Small orange-coloured animal; popular pet (8)
8 Not awake; in dreamland (6)
9 Hairpiece; toupee (3)
10 Way in or out (4)

Time ....

Puzzle 96

Across

1 Give up time for free; charity work (9)

5 Large heavy gun; used in warfare and fires balls (6)

6 Doctor ___ travels through time and space in an old police box (3)

7 Someone who is aged between thirteen and nineteen (4)

9 Amusing (5)

10 The sound a pig makes (4)

12 The joint between your thigh and your lower leg (4)

13 Conceals from view (5)

Down

1 American word for holiday (8)

2 Container with a light inside that can be held or hung up (7)

3 Midday (4)

4 Swap (8)

8 Dips in liquid (5)

11 Young goat or child (3)

 Time ....

Puzzle 97

Across
1 Elaborate and expensive (5)
4 Opposite of fast (4)
5 Red is the ___ of Santa's outfit (6)
6 Wheeled carriage for pushing a baby around (4)
8 Alligator (abbr) (5)
10 Operates the flying controls of an aircraft (5)
11 Special public event during which there are different types of performances (4)
13 Formal address (6)

Down
1 Posh dress (5)
2 Remove (3, 3)
3 Type of dance where people hold each other's waists and move forward in single file (5)
4 Something unexpected or astonishing (8)
7 Sporting contest (5)
8 Chew on something for a long time (4)
9 Operation (abbr) (2)
12 Used in comparison (2)

Time ....

Puzzle 98

Across

1 Moving; emotional (8)
5 Clumps of snow pressed together, used for throwing (8)
7 Physical education (inits) (2)
9 Clever; well dressed (5)
11 "Oh what fun it is to ride on a ___-___ open sleigh" (3, 5)
13 "Once ___ Royal David's City" (2)
14 Better or different from what is ordinary or usual (7)

Down

2 Object that is beautiful rather than useful (8)
3 Giant movie screen (4)
4 Swallow quickly or in large mouthfuls (4)
6 Have or show a strong feeling of respect for a god (7)
8 Large flightless Australian bird with a long neck (3)
10 Japanese dish made from rice topped with strips of raw fish or vegetables (5)
12 Single item or number (3)

 Time ....

Puzzle 99

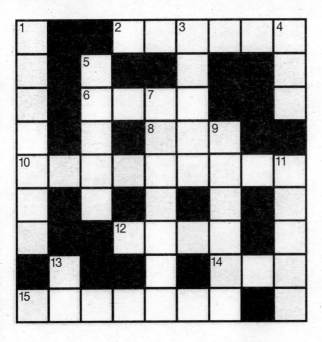

Across

2 Rides a bicycle (6)

6 The fleshy part of your ear (4)

8 Estimated time of arrival (inits) (3)

10 Plant which is traditionally hung up at Christmas; people kiss under it (9)

12 White salty Greek cheese made from sheep's or goat's milk (4)

14 Sound made by a pigeon or dove (3)

15 Give new strength or energy to something (7)

Down

1 "Little ___ Boy", or band member (7)

3 Largest of the Greek islands (5)

4 Droop; sink down (3)

5 Smooth, shiny appearance on the surface of something (5)

7 Have faith in (7)

9 Join or fasten to something else (6)

11 Electronic version of a book or magazine (5)

13 "___ Wish You a Merry Christmas" (2)

Time ....

Puzzle 100

Across

1 Near or next to (2)
3 Regarding (inits) (2)
4 The amount of people or things that will fit into a car (7)
7 Tin food container (3)
8 Male sheep (3)
9 "On the first day of Christmas ___ true love gave to me" (2)
11 Italian river; flows into the Adriatic sea (2)
12 Free time; relaxation (7)

Down

1 Brother (abbr) (3)
2 Period of 365 days (4)
4 Sugar heated until it turns brown; used as a flavouring in food or drink (7)
5 "Chestnuts roasting on ___ open fire" (2)
6 The period between sunrise and sunset (7)
9 Members of Parliament (inits) (3)
10 Used for the one being addressed (3)

 Time ....

Puzzle 101

Across

1 Percussion instrument played by pressing white and black keys (5)
4 Let or make something fall (4)
6 Your parent's sister (6)
7 Very quick (4)
9 Consumed; had a meal (3)
10 Long, narrow strip of cloth that is pleated and sewn on to the edge of a piece of clothing (5)
11 Type of play usually performed in schools around Christmas time (8)

Down

2 Chewy sweet made of nuts or dried fruit pieces; a traditional Christmas sweet in Italy (6)
3 Word used in a formal invitation (9)
4 One of Santa's reindeers whose name comes from the German word for thunder (6)
5 Very good; large in size (5)
7 Young deer (4)
8 Place to sit (4)

Time ....

Puzzle 102

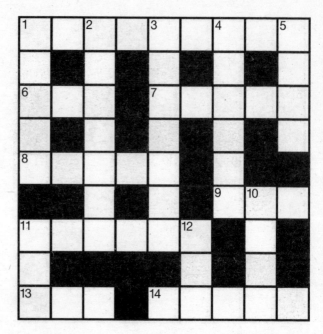

Across

1 Space in a room for a fire to burn (9)
6 Signed document acknowledging a debt (inits) (3)
7 Cut roast meat into slices (5)
8 Not moving (5)
9 Female sheep (3)
11 Language spoken in Denmark (6)
13 To burst (3)
14 Opposite of full (5)

Down

1 How Rudolph the Reindeer travels through the air (5)
2 People getting together after a long period apart (7)
3 Relishes made of vegetables or fruit preserved in vinegar or salt water (7)
4 Reach a place (6)
5 Opposite of odd (4)
10 To stand in line (4)
11 Lower something into a liquid briefly (3)
12 Sing a tune while keeping your lips closed (3)

 Time ....

Puzzle 103

Across

1 Pleasant smell; usually of a perfume or cologne (9)

5 Look forward to; await (6)

6 "___ the Most Wonderful Time of the Year" (3)

8 Top of the milk; often eaten with fruit and desserts (5)

12 Famous museum in Paris; home of the "Mona Lisa" (6)

13 Cities around the world hold this type of display to mark the beginning of the new year (8)

Down

1 Type of hens in "The Twelve Days of Christmas" (6)

2 Type of snake (3)

3 Against; opposed to (4)

4 Small beds with high barred sides usually for babies (4)

7 Man's dinner jacket worn at formal events (6)

9 Small image or symbol; used to express a feeling in electronic communication (5)

10 Cinema film (5)

11 Bit of inspiration (5)

Time ....

Puzzle 104

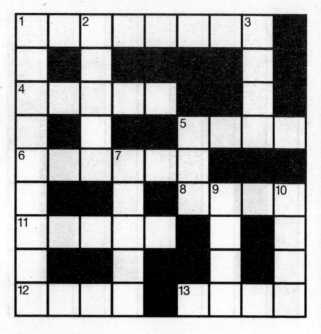

Across

1 Merry-go-round at a fair (8)

4 Building where monks or nuns live supervised by an abbot or abbess (5)

5 "___ In a Manger" (4)

6 Made by churning cream that can be spread on bread or used for frying (6)

8 Short journey; stumble (4)

11 Regal; kingly or queenly (5)

12 Open your mouth wide and take in a deep breath (4)

13 Broad smile (4)

Down

1 Red berry used to make sauce; traditionally served with the turkey on Christmas Day (9)

2 Machine that can be programmed to perform certain tasks like a human (5)

3 Molten rock that flows from a volcano (4)

5 Way to express yourself creatively (3)

7 Mode of transport (5)

9 Sound that a lion makes (4)

10 Detailed scheme or proposal for doing something (4)

 Time ....

Puzzle 105

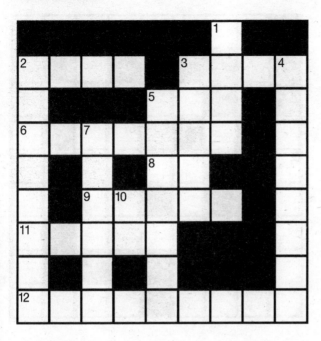

Across

2 Composed (4)

3 Like Pinocchio, eventually (4)

5 Small thin piece of metal with a sharp point (3)

6 Clear precious stone (7)

8 Title used before a woman's surname (2)

9 When something becomes mature (5)

11 In Victorian times this bird was the most popular dish to serve on Christmas Day (5)

12 Custom or belief that has been passed down through the generations (9)

Down

1 Pop in the mail (4)

2 Mass attended on Christmas Eve night by Christians (8)

3 Use water to remove dirt or soap from something (5)

4 Small house made from pieces of tree trunks and branches (3, 5)

5 Italian town that was buried under ash when Mount Vesuvius erupted (7)

7 Coloured light in the sky; the goddess of dawn (6)

10 "Born ___ the King of Israel" (2)

Time ....

Puzzle 106

Across

1 System of faith and worship (8)
5 See animals in the wild (6)
7 Mend (3)
8 Type of reflex (3)
9 Male cow (2)
10 Sauce or pickle that you eat with other food to give it more flavour (6)
12 Person who only likes and respects people who have a high social position (4)
13 Shopping ___ (5)
14 Sacred; religious (4)
15 Word to use at the beginning of a letter (4)

Down

1 Edited version of an original piece of music (5)
2 Picture (5)
3 Create in your mind (7)
4 The person who lives next door to you (9)
6 Opposite of true (5)
7 In "The Twelve Days of Christmas" calling birds were given on this day (6)
10 Do something in return (5)
11 "Rudolph with your nose ___ bright" (2)

 Time ....

Puzzle 107

Across

4 "Much ___ About Nothing", a play by Shakespeare (3)

6 Female child (4)

8 Make something look more attractive by adding things to it (8)

9 Be in a suitable place; somewhere where you are happy (6)

10 Heroic and extraordinary (4)

11 Wild animal; Beauty's admirer (5)

12 An elephant's nose (5)

13 Type of poem that expresses the writer's feelings about a particular person or thing (3)

Down

1 Young boy (3)

2 One of Snow White's seven dwarves (3)

3 Illuminated or burning (3)

5 The month in which Christmas occurs (8)

6 Small mechanical or electronic device (6)

7 To be given something (8)

Time ....

Puzzle 108

Across

1 Feel or show great joy or delight (7)
5 Young child, baby or toddler (3)
7 Jealousy (4)
8 "Deck the ___ with boughs of holly" (5)
9 Rose from sleep (4)
11 Soft (6)
12 Long time; grows old (4)
13 Measure the duration of (4)
14 Small thin branches of a tree (5)

Down

2 Retail stores; air vents (7)
3 Glossy, hard brown nuts; often roasted and eaten in winter (9)
4 Buttons on a board that you press to operate a computer (4)
5 An idea or opinion formed by thinking (7)
6 Large tree that bears acorns (3)
10 Grins from ear to ear (5)

Time ....

Puzzle 109

Across

3 Iron or steel becomes this when it reacts with air or water (5)

5 Assists (5)

6 Friend (3)

9 Take part in a special activity or social gathering to show that a particular occasion is important (9)

10 Disc that can play recorded sound (inits) (2)

11 Device for giving light (4)

14 Narrow sledge usually made from wood, the front of which curves up and backward (8)

Down

1 Sweet treat; made from cacao seeds (9)

2 Ski race between flag poles (6)

3 Society that protects birds (inits) (4)

4 Cold dish made from a mixture of fruits or vegetables (5)

7 Curved part of a building that is over an opening (4)

8 An untidy pile or mass of things (4)

12 Opposite of rich (4)

13 Adult male (3)

Time ....

Puzzle 110

Across

1 Mix with a spoon; begin to move (4)

5 Large area of land with grass and trees where children can play (4)

6 "___ dreaming of a white Christmas" (2)

7 Little hungry (7)

9 Thank you, informally (2)

10 Rich, deep red colour (7)

11 "Merry Christmas and Happy ___ ___" (3, 4)

Down

2 Group of players forming one side in a competitive game or sport (4)

3 Another name for Jesus (6)

4 Traditional stories and culture of a group of people passed down through the generations (8)

5 Make a small hole in something (6)

7 Something you win (5)

8 Part of the deal (4)

 Time ....

Puzzle 111

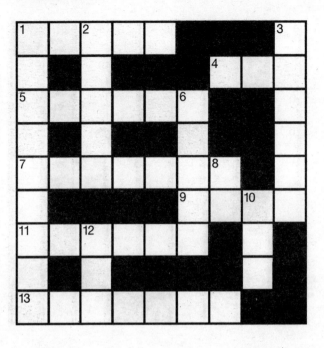

Across

1 Groups of musicians who play music together (5)
4 Entertaining and enjoyable (3)
5 Surprises greatly; fills with astonishment (6)
7 Shop might put this up in its window at Christmas time (7)
9 Wear a scarf to warm this part of your body (4)
11 Deeply loved (6)
13 Enthusiastic; how many children feel on Christmas Eve (7)

Down

1 Tabletop game that involves moving counters around a pre-marked surface (5, 4)
2 Gets closer to (5)
3 Waterproof jacket (6)
6 Opposite of sit (5)
8 "Oh Come All ___ Faithful" (2)
10 Taxi (3)
12 Evil goblin in J.R.R Tolkien's "The Lord of the Rings" (3)

Time ....

Puzzle 112

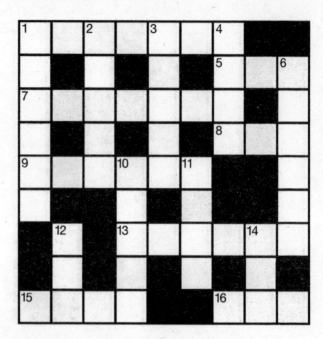

Across

1 Ways to thank or ask for help from a god (7)

5 Heavy sharp tool; use to chop wood (3)

7 Feelings such as happiness, fear or anger (7)

8 Use a shovel to do this (3)

9 Make a journey (6)

13 Portable computer (6)

15 Opposite of take (4)

16 Alien spaceship (inits) (3)

Down

1 More than enough (6)

2 Strong, pleasant smell (5)

3 An electronic invitation by email or text (5)

4 Build castles from this on a beach (4)

6 Small container for holding a boiled egg (6)

10 How much something is worth (5)

11 Facial feature (4)

12 Large colourful Japanese carp fish kept in ponds (3)

14 Opposite of on (3)

Time ....

Puzzle 113

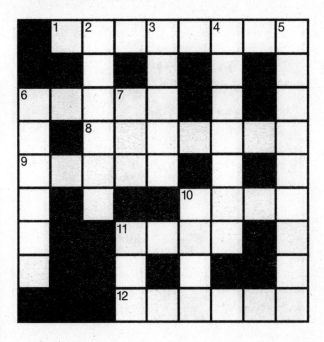

Across

1 Liquid for mixing into a salad to give it more flavour (8)
6 String or cord made up of two or more strands of material twisted together (5)
8 No sound (7)
9 Question thoroughly; cook using direct heat (5)
10 Car whose driver you can pay to drive you to your destination (4)
11 Grumble or complain (4)
12 Sections or fragments (6)

Down

2 Dried grape (6)
3 Hard outer case of an egg or sea creature (5)
4 Superhero who fights villains in a powered suit of armour (4, 3)
5 Words of welcome (9)
6 Close-fitting garment; ballet attire (6)
7 Nothing (3)
10 Measuring strip; can be sticky (4)
11 Cleaning tool for wiping floors (3)

Time ....

Puzzle 114

Across

1 State of feeling bored (7)
5 Cabbage with crinkled leaves, contain lots of Vitamin K (4)
7 Mixture to put inside a turkey before roasting (8)
11 UK honour, given by the Queen (inits) (3)
12 To give amusement or enjoyment (9)
13 Connected with poetry (6)
15 Energy of the sun (5)

Down

2 Belonging to us (4)
3 All right (inits) (2)
4 Enchanting (7)
6 Block of something with six sides (4)
8 Walk unsteadily as if about to fall over (6)
9 Show wheel; common fairground ride (6)
10 Warm spice; hair colour (6)
14 Chemical symbol for cobalt (2)

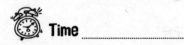

Time ....

Puzzle 115

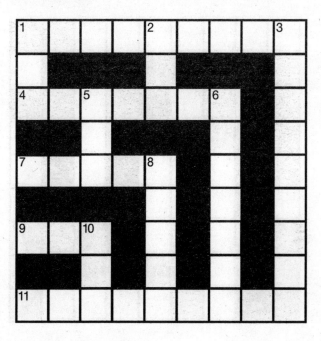

Across

1 Storm during which pellets of frozen rain fall (9)

4 Used to soak in hot water (7)

7 Small ornament worn on a bracelet (5)

9 Piece of crockery that you can drink from (3)

11 Bought (9)

Down

1 Centre of a wheel (3)

2 Game, ___ and match; common phrase used in tennis (3)

3 Amazed by; filled with wonder (9)

5 Information to come (inits) (3)

6 Loud; explosive firework (7)

8 Eat something noisily (5)

10 Term used in golf (3)

Time ....

Puzzle 116

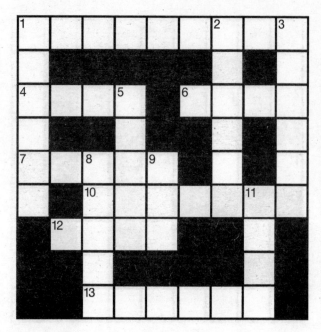

Across

1 Existing everywhere; involving everyone (9)

4 Popular meat; grievance (4)

6 Bring bad luck; cast an evil spell (4)

7 In front of; in the lead (5)

10 Doing something while making very little noise (7)

12 Naked (4)

13 Deciduous trees are ones that lose these in winter (6)

Down

1 Energetic; lively (6)

2 Ghost (6)

3 Great comfort provided by expensive things (6)

5 Using deception and trickery to take something valuable from someone (5)

8 The same as (5)

9 Cube that rolls (3)

11 Thick pieces of a tree trunk or branch that are used for burning or building (4)

 Time ....

Puzzle 117

Across

1 An outer garment worn to stay warm and dry (4)
4 Flexible pipe through which water flows; used for watering plants and fighting fires (4)
7 Dull, continuous pain (4)
8 Hollow pipe; toothpaste container (4)
10 Exclamation; in pain (2)
11 Scottish New Year celebrations (8)
12 Sensitivity; can cause sneezing or a rash (7)

Down

1 Collide violently (5)
2 Wear this under your clothes, designed to keep you warm (7)
3 Sprouted; like a weed (4)
5 Astonishing; very attractive (8)
6 Political union (inits) (2)
9 Young man or male child (3)

Time ....

ADVANCED

Across

1 Handle that you use to open or close a door (8)
3 Portion of bread, usually sliced (4)
4 Strong wind (4)
6 Male sibling (7)
8 Young sheep (4)
10 Soft shiny material that is made from the threads produced by certain insects (4)
11 Serious, urgent or heartfelt request (6)

Down

1 Small model of a human figure; used as a child's toy (4)
2 Classical dance such as "Swan Lake" and "The Nutcracker" (6)
5 Part of a house (4)
6 Cindrella's soiree (4)
7 Covering for your face; a disguise to amuse or frighten others (4)
9 Also known as (inits) (3)

Time ....

Puzzle 119

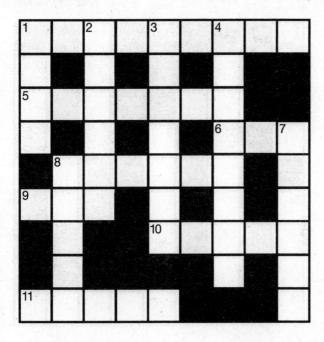

Across
1 Yuletide dessert (9)
5 Full of energy and life; a strong and bright colour (7)
6 Covered with frozen water; very cold (3)
8 Snow does this when it is blown by the wind into high piles (6)
9 Container for rubbish (3)
10 Patient of a pediatrician (5)
11 Colour of pine needles (5)

Down
1 Number of gold rings in "The Twelve Days of Christmas" (4)
2 Not yet come into the world; a baby in the womb (6)
3 Movement of vehicles along a route (7)
4 Having a natural skill; known to be creative (8)
7 Distant but within sight (6)
8 Restaurant serving American food (5)

Time ....

Puzzle 120

Across

4 Menu item; plate (4)

6 Type of thick, soft cloth made from a pressed mass of wool, often used in crafting (4)

7 Hot liquid rock found below the surface of the earth (5)

9 Ultraviolet (inits) (2)

11 Miserly character (7)

13 University (abbr) (3)

14 Sign off a letter to someone (9)

Down

1 Female spouse (4)

2 Male ruler; Wenceslas (4)

3 Not what it seems to be (8)

5 Divine; giving great pleasure (8)

7 Small glass ball used in children's games (6)

8 Something to drink tea out of (3)

10 Character in boots (4)

12 Thick substance flowing slowly out of something (4)

 Time ....

Puzzle 121

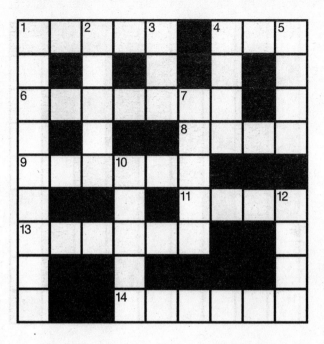

Across

1 Stomach (5)
4 Little lie (3)
6 Glimmer of light (7)
8 Formal test to show your knowledge in a subject (4)
9 Traditional story that has been passed down through the generations (6)
11 Sharp intake of breath (4)
13 Lacking pride (6)
14 Wrinkly, brown edible nut (6)

Down

1 The town where Jesus was born in the Bible (9)
2 Resting position (5)
3 Long-haired cattle (3)
4 Bend a muscle (4)
5 The edge around the bottom of a hat (4)
7 Narrow shelf that sticks out from a wall, window or cliff (5)
10 Joint in your arm (5)
12 Push your lower lip forward to show annoyance (4)

Time ....

Puzzle 122

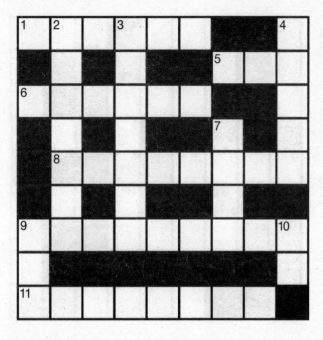

Across

1 Away from the right path or direction (6)
5 At a great distance (3)
6 US term for football (6)
8 The ability to wait for a long time without complaining (8)
9 Extremely intelligent or skilled at something (9)
11 Willing to give money, help or time more than is usual or expected (8)

Down

2 Individual who is looking for things to buy (7)
3 Performance of music or poetry (7)
4 Three-wheeled bike (5)
7 Old Indian coin (4)
9 Important shopper's item (3)
10 Electronic device to watch shows (abbr) (2)

 Time ....

Puzzle 123

Across

1 Water turning into ice (8)
5 Set of cube-shaped pieces used for building toys (6)
6 Monument for keeping or remembering (4)
8 The soft, thick hair that grows on the bodies of sheep (4)
10 Become limp and weak; bend towards the ground (4)
12 Star sign represented by a lion (3)
13 When frozen flakes of water fall from the sky (7)

Down

1 Move behind someone and go where they go (6)
2 Extremely good (9)
3 Skin of a citrus fruit; can be added to give flavour (4)
4 Worldwide (6)
7 Single-piece garment (6)
9 Van Gogh paintings (4)
11 As well; also (3)

Time ....

Puzzle 124

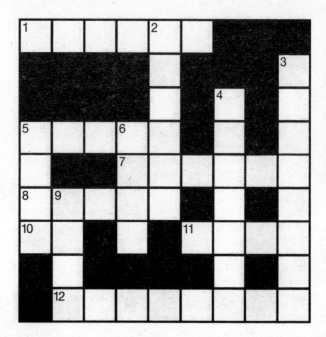

Across

1 Late morning meal; breakfast with lunch (6)

5 Cuts into small cubes (5)

7 Make a liquid thinner by adding water to it (6)

8 Someone who doesn't eat any meat or food that comes from animals (5)

10 Edward (abbr) (2)

11 Money in the form of notes or coins (4)

12 Month of Bonfire Night (8)

Down

2 The child of your aunt or uncle (6)

3 With each other (8)

4 Long red and green stemmed plant, eaten in crumbles (7)

5 White bird, a symbol of peace (4)

6 Hard, round, mild-tasting Dutch cheese (4)

9 The garden where, according to the Bible, the very first humans lived (4)

 Time ....

Puzzle 125

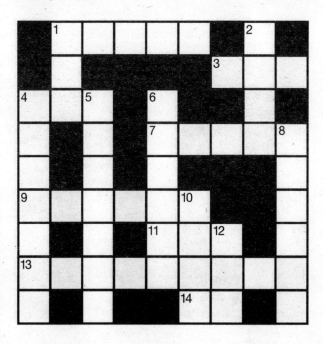

Across

1 Large or fierce fire (5)
3 Babies wear this when they eat (3)
4 Popular music; words are spoken quickly and rhythmically (3)
7 Long, loose piece of outer clothing (5)
9 Delay doing something (3, 3)
11 Rule; usually made by a government (3)
13 Work together to make something happen (9)
14 Milligram (abbr) (2)

Down

1 Sound made by a sheep (3)
2 Move from a lower position to a higher one (4)
4 To treat courteously (7)
5 Part; serving (7)
6 Cold dessert made of layers (6)
8 Small, round and shallow dish to hold a cup (6)
10 Grow crops; cultivate land (4)
12 Dog's tail (3)

Time

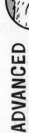

Puzzle 126

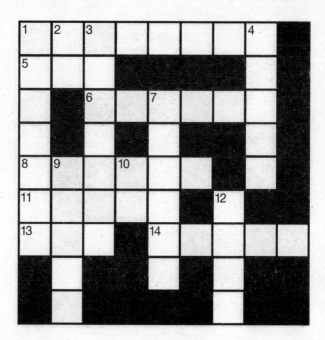

Across

1 Desire for food (8)
5 Home improvement project (inits) (3)
6 Court entertainer (6)
8 Romantic comedy (abbr) (6)
11 Shared spaghetti with Lady (5)
13 Sister (abbr) (3)
14 Feeling pleased and satisfied because you or someone close to you has achieved something (5)

Down

1 Short clips promoting products (7)
2 Private investigator (inits) (2)
3 Loose fitting top and trousers for sleeping in (7)
4 Before the usual or expected time (5)
7 Not taking care or making an effort (6)
9 Mythical hunter; constellation (5)
10 Chemical symbol for curium (2)
12 Middle part of an egg (4)

Time ....

Puzzle 127

ADVANCED

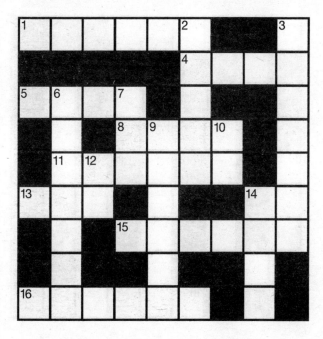

Across

1 Opposite of staying still (6)
4 List of names; used at work (4)
5 Electric vehicle (4)
8 Solemn promise (4)
11 Shops on Christmas Day (6)
13 Bunny's movement (3)
14 "So Do La ___ Mi Do Re"; song lyrics from "The Sound of Music" (2)
15 There are eleven of these piping in "The Twelve Days of Christmas" (6)
16 Make something new (6)

Down

2 Rub a food against small sharp edges to shred it (5)
3 Pieces of equipment for taking pictures (7)
6 Get over an illness (7)
7 Sound a cow makes (3)
9 Help (6)
10 High definition (inits) (2)
12 An album (inits) (2)
14 No charge (4)

Time

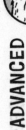

ADVANCED

Across

1 Finger-shaped pastry filled with cream and covered with chocolate (6)
5 One of your five senses (5)
7 Made, created, brought into existence (8)
13 Sound of giggling (3)
14 Stays where it is; what is left (7)
15 Star that is the centre of our solar system (3)
16 Phone that you can carry wherever you go (6)

Down

2 Hands together (4)
3 Information technology (inits) (2)
4 Pasta sauce made with meat and tomatoes (4)
6 Pre-adolescent (5)
8 Broadcast before and is being shown again (5)
9 Spotted rectangular tile; used in a popular game (6)
10 Red or green pepper that has a very hot taste (6)
11 Strong wish to have or do something (6)
12 Middle part of your body above your hips (5)

Time ....

Puzzle 129

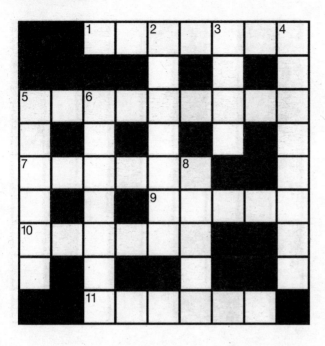

Across

1 Allow yourself to have or do something desirable (7)

5 Important events, ceremonies or celebrations (9)

7 Small folded case to keep cash and cards (6)

9 Sharp tool for shaving (5)

10 Responds (6)

11 Covered in dirty wet snow; something romantic and sentimental (6)

Down

2 Sweet dish that you eat at the end of a meal (7)

3 See; watch (4)

4 Wind that blows from the East (8)

5 Going forward (6)

6 Neck bands (7)

8 Items on a to-do list (5)

Time ....

Puzzle 130

Across

2 Fine; delicate (4)
4 Feeling of affection (4)
6 Our planet (5)
7 Room at the top
   of the house (5)
9 Painter's frame (5)
11 Brush with a long handle; used
   for sweeping the floor (5)
12 Part of a BLT sandwich (5)
14 Spree or period of doing
   too much of something (5)
15 Make identical in sound (5)

Down

1 Black powder that rises
   in the smoke from a fire
   and collects on the inside
   of chimneys (4)
3 Plants whose leaves are
   used in cooking to add
   flavour (5)
5 Twelfth month; time
   to be festive (8)
8 Doctor Who's transport (6)
10 Sudden forward motion (5)
13 Weep, sob (3)

Time ....

Puzzle 131

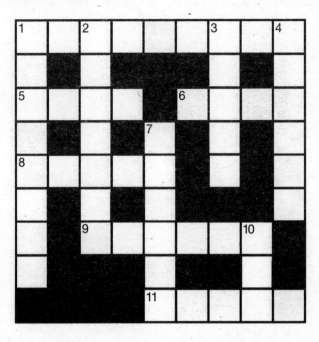

Across

1 Cherished or prized possessions (9)
5 Ridge of jagged rock or coral near the surface of the sea (4)
6 Genre of music since 1920s (4)
8 Country of origin of panettone (5)
9 Magician performs these (6)
11 Thin, hollow tube through which you can suck a drink into your mouth (5)

Down

1 Extraordinarily great (8)
2 Gracefully stylish and dignified (7)
3 Fully prepared (5)
4 To overpower by intense light; extremely impressive (6)
7 The words of a song (6)
10 Ocean (3)

Time

Puzzle 132

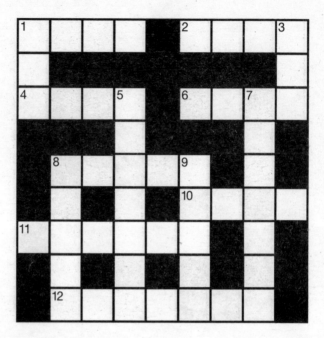

Across

1 Mild common illness (4)
2 "'Twas the night before Christmas", first line of a famous ___ about Santa visiting a house on Christmas Eve (4)
4 The person in charge (4)
6 Red gemstone (4)
8 Long-running serialized TV dramas (5)
10 Feeling that somewhere on your body needs scratching (4)
11 Move in an energetic and busy way (6)
12 Without any flaws (7)

Down

1 Baby lion (3)
3 "And ___ all your Christmases be white" (3)
5 The first course of a three-course meal (7)
7 Cookie (7)
8 Slouch down, especially in front of the television (5)
9 Sift (5)

Time ....

Puzzle 133

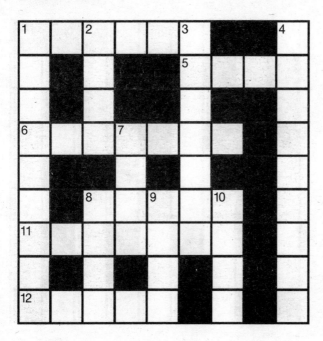

Across

1 ___ Santa, the tradition in which members of a group randomly select one person to buy a Christmas gift for (6)

5 An enclosed compartment for baking or roasting food (4)

6 The money that something costs you (7)

8 Remove a liquid from something by making it flow somewhere else (5)

11 Scandinavian pastry, a Nordic variety of pretzel (7)

12 Reigned over (5)

Down

1 Person who makes footwear as a profession (9)

2 Cage or pen; somewhere you keep chickens (4)

3 Uppermost layer of soil (7)

4 Vehicle that slides down snowy hills (9)

7 Receive money in return for the work that you do (4)

8 Key in a telephone number to make a call (4)

9 Very old (4)

10 Immediately afterwards (4)

Time

Puzzle 134

Across

1 Baby birds (6)
5 Objects used to keep a row of books standing upright (4)
7 Believe that someone is good and honest (5)
8 Squirrel wraps this part of its body around itself to keep warm in cold weather (4)
9 From Switzerland (5)
12 "Hark the herald angels sing, glory to the ___ King" (7)
14 Bead formed inside the shells of some sea creatures (5)
16 Getting good food regularly (4, 3)

Down

2 Opposite of cold (3)
3 Route followed (6)
4 Badger's home (4)
6 Magnificent; very impressive (8)
9 Exchange (4)
10 Member of your husband's or wife's family (5)
11 Become larger and rounder than usual (5)
13 Count of Lemony Snicket (4)
15 Study of religion (inits) (2)

 Time ....

Puzzle 135

Across

5 Mexican dish made up of strips of meat and vegetables wrapped in a tortilla (6)

7 South West (inits) (2)

9 Brown rodent (3)

10 Number of dwarves that befriended Snow White (5)

11 Pull open a bow or knot (5)

13 Type of tree that has leaves that fall in winter and wood that is used to make furniture (3)

15 Opposite of down (2)

16 England's national flower (4)

17 Drink that has bubbles (5)

Down

1 Show an unnecessary amount of worry (4)

2 Feel concern or interest (4)

3 Small piece or amount of something (3)

4 Scottish musical instrument (7)

6 The first month of the year (7)

8 In good health (4)

12 Long walrus teeth (5)

14 System of paths between walls or hedges designed to confuse people (4)

Time ....

Puzzle 136

Across

2 Sweet, yellow sauce made from milk and eggs (7)

6 To stop blaming someone for something they have done wrong (7)

8 Journal; write thoughts about daily life events (5)

10 Hot beverage made from ground beans (6)

11 Clean an area by brushing away dirt (5)

12 Lazy; avoiding work (4)

13 The person telling a story (8)

Down

1 Gentle feeling of fondness or liking (9)

2 Trying to avoid damaging something or making a mistake (7)

3 Water park attractions (6)

4 Region (4)

5 Responsibility; obligation (4)

7 Opinion (4)

9 Lively Scottish dance (4)

 Time ....

Puzzle 137

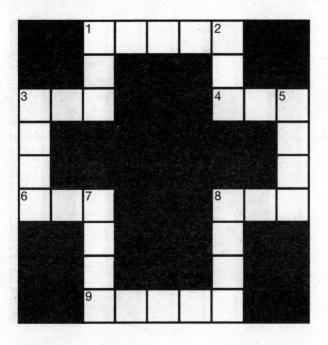

Across

1 Wobbly dessert; made by setting liquid gelatin in a mould (5)
3 "Remember Christ ___ Savior was born on Christmas Day" (3)
4 Long bench used by worshippers in a church (3)
6 Doctor (abbr) (3)
8 When a baby is expected to be born (3)
9 Passage between a row of seats in a building such as a church or theatre (5)

Down

1 Container for jam (3)
2 High barking sound made by a small dog (3)
3 Needed to pay or repay in return for something received (4)
5 Drink made from grapes (4)
7 Popular fizzy pop (4)
8 Sleep lightly (4)

Time

Puzzle 138

Across

2 First appearance of daylight in the morning (4)
4 King of Judea (5)
7 Topping of banoffee pie (6)
9 Skirt worn by a ballerina (4)
11 Grand chair sat on by royalty (6)
13 An animal that you keep at home and care for (3)
14 Provide an opportunity (5)

Down

1 Set on fire again (5)
2 Feeling of uncertainty (5)
3 Public promotion of a product (abbr) (2)
5 Large piece of cloth made of warm material (7)
6 Fastest pace of a horse (6)
8 Professional writer (6)
10 Dorothy's dog in "The Wizard of Oz" (4)
12 Opposite of old (3)

 Time ....

Puzzle 139

Across

1 Of an acceptable standard or quality (6)
5 Line that carries water or gas (4)
6 Moving with elegance in an attractive way (5)
8 Gesture of the head (7)
10 Snuggle into a warm and comfortable position (6)
12 The first name of Scrooge, the main character in "A Christmas Carol" (8)

Down

1 "___ ___ Merrily on High" (4, 4)
2 Opposite of dirty (5)
3 Called (5)
4 Mischievous type of fairy (5)
7 The amount of money needed to buy, do or make something (4)
9 Someone who plays a lot of computer games (5)
11 Cry (3)

Time ....

Puzzle 140

Across

4 "Hark the ___ Angels Sing" (6)
6 Number of legs on a spider (5)
8 Turned into ice (6)
10 Partner of tic and toe (3)
11 Head of a tribe or clan (5)
13 ___ Rowling; the author of the Harry Potter books (inits) (2)
14 Recall, recollect, reminisce (8)

Down

1 Move position (5)
2 Decorative pin, often worn to hold clothing in place (6)
3 Soft warm fabric used to make tops and jackets (6)
5 Loud horrible noise (3)
7 Covered basket; containing a variety of foods (6)
9 Noisy disturbance (6)
12 Extremely good (abbr) (3)
13 Young members of staff (abbr) (2)

 Time ....

Puzzle 141

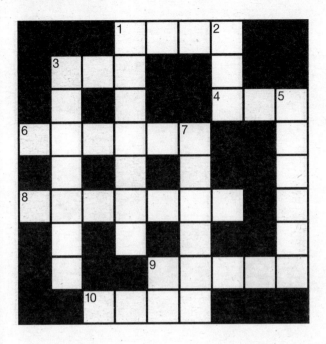

Across

1 Stage performance, especially a musical (4)
3 Metal container used for cooking in (3)
4 Tiny drops of water that form on cool surfaces at night (3)
6 Young child or baby (6)
8 Eager to know or learn something (7)
9 Construct (5)
10 Opposite of comes (4)

Down

1 Enter quietly trying not to be noticed (5, 2)
2 To be married (3)
3 Black and white flightless bird (7)
5 Feet that have skin between the toes (6)
7 Sign of the zodiac represented by a bull (6)
9 "'Tis the season to ___ jolly" (2)

Time ....

Puzzle 142

Across

1 "God Rest Ye Merry ___" (9)
6 Legally take a child into your family and raise it as your own (5)
7 Name given to a book (5)
8 Aunt's husband (5)
11 Deep sleep; state of unconsciousness (4)
12 Edged with hanging narrow strips of material or threads (7)

Down

1 Charm and allure (7)
2 Corner or part of a room that is cut off from the rest (4)
3 "Oh ___ Town of Bethlehem" (6)
4 Arrange or happen to get together (4)
5 Island where Peter Pan and the Lost Boys live (9)
9 Professional cook (4)
10 Opposite of short (4)

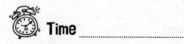

Time ....

Puzzle 143

Across
1 Soft like wool or fur (6)
5 Chances of something happening (4)
6 Arcade coin (5)
7 Turn over quickly (4)
9 Place where you catch a flight (7)
11 Sound a cat makes (4)
12 Loud shout (4)

Down
1 Best liked; most enjoyed (9)
2 Opposite of over (5)
3 Style of singing where your voice keeps on going up and down (5)
4 Public transport vehicle (3)
7 Boat or ship that transports passengers or goods (5)
8 Coloured part of a flower that attracts insects (5)
10 Dog's foot (3)

Time ....

Puzzle 144

Across

1 In bed with the sheets pulled tightly around you (6, 2)

7 Sound (5)

9 Person or animal who you spend a lot of time with (9)

11 Small single-storey house (3)

12 Completely (7)

13 Quick light touch with your hand (3)

14 Innate; unaffected (7)

Down

2 Colourful card game (3)

3 Noisy disturbance (9)

4 Short nap (3)

5 First to land a probe on a comet (inits) (3)

6 Small hollow mark (4)

8 Nautical speed unit (4)

9 Comfortably happy (7)

10 Interlaced hair (5)

11 Overactive (5)

Time ....

Level Four:
Ace Puzzlers

Puzzle 145

ACE PUZZLERS

Across

1 Container for liquids (5)
3 Light, silly laugh (6)
6 Difficult to bite through; tough (5)
7 "O'er the fields we ___ , laughing all the way" (2)
8 Small green or yellow plant that grows in clumps in damp places (4)
10 Without holes, lumps or bumps (6)
12 Preparing hot meals (7)
13 Eat hastily; wild pack animal (4)
14 "And ___ you ever saw it, you would even say it glows" (2)
15 Considerate of the feelings of others (10)

Down

1 Small number of (3)
2 Nearly (6)
4 Long, elegant dresses worn on formal occasions (5)
5 Very pretty (9)
6 Magazine containing stories told in pictures (5)
7 Thick, sticky substance (3)
8 The part of the day from when the sun rises to noon (7)
9 Try to attract attention or admiration in a way that others find annoying (4, 3)
11 Force air out of your lungs with a harsh sound to clear your throat (5)
13 Ability to use words or ideas in a clever, funny or imaginative way (3)

Time ....

ACE PUZZLERS

Puzzle 146

Across

4 Not cold (3)
5 Container used in the garden (3)
7 ___ boot sale is an event where people can sell the things they don't want anymore (3)
8 An activity you do regularly in your leisure time (5)
11 Small biting insect that can jump high (4)
12 Small sharp bites or pinches (4)
13 Opposite of wrong (5)
15 Animal that is like a monkey but has no tail (3)
17 Coconut ___ is a funfair attraction in which the aim is to knock coconuts down from poles (3)
19 Small naughty elf or spirit (3)

Down

1 Two performers who work together (3)
2 Tool for detangling and arranging hair (4)
3 Edible, small green seed found in a pod (3)
6 Building where plays and other performances are staged (7)
7 Young swans (7)
9 Type of sandwich (inits) (3)
10 Measure of speed; in miles (inits) (3)
14 Precious stones (4)
16 Collection of pieces of paper that are fastened together along one side for writing or drawing on (3)
18 The bottom edge of a piece of cloth that is folded over and sewn so that there are no loose threads (3)

Time ....

ACE PUZZLERS

Puzzle 147

ACE PUZZLERS

Across

1 Sneaky; deceitful (3)
2 Evergreen tree that produces cones (7)
7 Fashion that takes inspiration from styles of the past (5)
8 With forward motion (5)
9 Postscript (inits) (2)
12 "Do ___ Know It's Christmas?" (4)
13 Meal cooked and bought at a shop but taken elsewhere to be eaten (8)
15 To cover most of a surface; to give someone so much attention that they feel uncomfortable (7)
17 Tool for playing snooker, billiards or pool (3)
18 Programme on your phone that enables it to perform a specific task (abbr) (3)
19 Wipe your feet on it (3)
20 Flat piece of paper with a sealable flap that can hold a letter or document (8)

Down

1 Sweet, thick liquid (5)
3 Biblical character who built an ark to survive a flood (4)
4 Drink topped with a foam of white bubbles (6)
5 Sport played with an oval-shaped ball (5)
6 Small ornament that isn't worth much (7)
10 Small piece of paper you stick on to an envelope or parcel to show how much postage you have paid (5)
11 Someone who supplies food for a party (7)
12 Device that controls the flow of water from a pipe (3)
14 Sweet, charming and pleasing (4)
15 Secure box in which you can keep your valuables (4)
16 Exposed to attack (4)
17 Short cloak sometimes worn by superheroes (4)
19 Chemical symbol for molybdenum (2)

Time ....

Puzzle 148

ACE PUZZLERS

Across

1 Using the oven (6)
3 Seas (6)
5 " ___ humbug" (3)
7 If someone ___ in, they wake up much later in the morning than they would normally do (6)
9 Break in half (5)
10 Piece of thick heavy cloth; used for covering the floor (3)
12 Display (abbr) (4)
13 Popular children's character; a tank engine (6)
16 Activities such as judo and jujutsu can be described as this kind of arts (7)
17 Dish of meat and vegetables cooked slowly in a closed pot (4)
18 Traditionally Scottish design for cloth (6)
19 Slightly rude but in a charming or amusing way (6)

Down

1 Look after a child or children while the parents are out (7)
2 When a ball is kicked into the back of a net (4)
4 Be grateful or thankful (10)
6 Common greeting when you meet someone (5)
7 Cook food by heating it in the vapour from boiling water (5)
8 Result of adding two or more numbers (3)
11 Mischievous, ugly, dwarf-like creature of folklore (6)
14 Wooden box with a wire front that is used for keeping small pets such as rabbits (5)
15 Type of water found in the sea (5)

Time

ACE PUZZLERS

Puzzle 149

ACE PUZZLERS

Across

3 Cloth made by weaving together threads of material such as cotton, nylon or silk (6)

5 Edible fish with pink flesh that swims up rivers against the current to lay eggs (6)

6 Fairy tales often end with the good characters living happily ever __ (5)

8 Leave (6)

10 Saint (abbr) (2)

12 Theatres where films are shown (7)

15 Mix a salad (4)

17 Damaged and shabby due to overuse (4)

18 Global organisation (inits) (2)

19 Decorative wool ball (3, 3)

20 Small piece of material with a hole through so it can be threaded on to a string or thin chain (4)

21 Crowd together; nestling closely (6)

Down

1 What you do to a snow globe to make the snow fall inside it (5)

2 Someone who admires and supports a band or team (3)

3 Finding a clover with this number of leaves is thought to be lucky (4)

4 Hard yellow cheese (7)

7 Wood that is burnt as fuel (8)

8 Hotel rooms often have a "Do not ___" sign (7)

9 Great victory or achievement (7)

11 If something is very heavy it can be said to weigh a ___ (3)

13 Mum in the USA (3)

14 Sleep-induced noise (5)

16 Potato, informally (4)

Time ....

ACE PUZZLERS

Puzzle 150

Across

1 Talk on a religious or moral subject, usually part of a Christian church ceremony (6)
6 Macarons and Bakewell tarts are flavoured with this nut (6)
7 Crumbly Scottish biscuit (10)
8 "On the first day of Christmas my true love sent to __" (2)
9 On the other hand; in other words (2)
10 Active bean (6)
14 Up to date (3)
16 The ___ Piper of Hamelin is a character of folklore who played a magic pipe (4)
17 Fabric cases filled with soft material used to sit or lean on (8)
18 You can use this to catch fish or make curtains (3)
19 Expensive (6)
20 Ancient stories that were made up to explain particular events or occurrences (5)

Down

2 Piece of soft rubber used to rub out something (6)
3 Events from the past that you can recall (8)
4 Chat continuously for a long time (6)
5 Breathed in (7)
8 Cut grass with a machine (3)
11 "It Came __ a Midnight Clear" (4)
12 The number of minutes in a football match (6)
13 Place where a bird lays its eggs and feeds its chicks (4)
14 Person trained to take care of the unwell (5)
15 " ___ Shepherds Watched Their Flocks" (5)

Time ....

Puzzle 151

ACE PUZZLERS

Across

1 Gathering of friends to drink and dance in someone's home (5, 5)
4 Items of cutlery used for eating, stirring and serving food (6)
6 Throw out suddenly and forcefully (5)
9 Easy to understand; without any blemishes or marks (5)
10 Warm up (4)
11 Pull along by a rope or chain (3)
12 Serious and official (6)
13 Give back (6)
15 Go in (5)
16 Young insect that has hatched out of its egg but has not yet developed into an adult (5)
17 Thick cold sauce made from tomatoes (7)

Down

1 Sudden calm silence (4)
2 Child who is badly behaved because they are pampered (6)
3 An actor's part in a play or film (4)
5 To add salt, herbs or pepper (6)
7 Low rank (abbr) (2)
8 A ___ box is a place where you keep useful items for fixing and building things (4)
9 Horse's pace that is in between a trot and a gallop (6)
10 Messenger (6)
11 Pastry case with no top that has a sweet or savoury filling (4)
12 Extremely unusual or unlikely (5)
14 Snow ___ is a type of white, bell-shaped flower (4)

Time ....

Puzzle 152

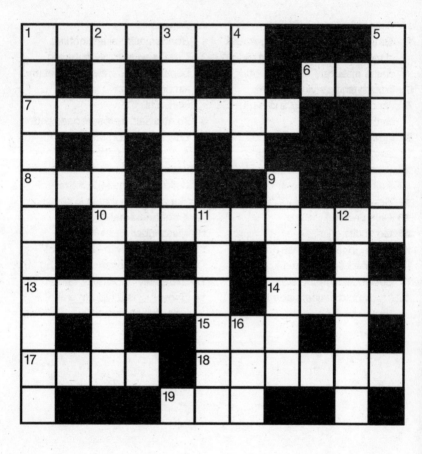

ACE PUZZLERS

Across

1 Serving yourself another portion of food after having eaten the first one is a second ___ (7)
6 French for yes (3)
7 Windy weather can be described as this (8)
8 Piece or scrap of old material (3)
10 Loveable and sweet (9)
13 ___ Questions is a yes or no guessing game (6)
14 "I don't want a lot for Christmas, there is just one thing I ___" (4)
15 To excess (inits) (3)
17 Expert in a particular subject (4)
18 Dry crackling sound (6)
19 Good to go (3)

Down

1 When an animal is sleeping through winter (11)
2 Comfortable clothing for wearing at home (6, 4)
3 Plan; aim (6)
4 Spiritual teacher or recognized leader in a particular subject (4)
5 At Christmas people usually sit around a ___ table (6)
9 Impression made on a surface by a person's fingertip (6)
11 Winnie the Pooh's donkey friend (6)
12 Thin, sharp tool used for knitting (6)
16 Short sound to show disapproval (3)

Time ....

ACE PUZZLERS

Puzzle 153

ACE PUZZLERS

Across

2 Star sign represented by a ram (5)
4 Artificial intelligence (inits) (2)
5 This sound repeated represents laughter (2)
7 Expresses approval or admiration (7)
10 An Italian dish made up of layers of pasta and mince with both cheese and tomato sauces (7)
12 " ___ Wish You a Merry Christmas" (2)
13 Compass point (inits) (2)
15 "Oh Come All ___ Faithful" (2)
16 Former partner (2)
17 Loose-skinned citrus fruit (9)

Down

1 Wireless internet (2, 2)
2 "Walking in the ___" (3)
3 Female pronoun (3)
4 Fruit that Eve gave to Adam according to the Bible (5)
6 Name of the lion in "The Lion, the Witch and the Wardrobe" (5)
8 Donkey (3)
9 To become weak and tired (3)
11 Mermaid princess in Disney's "The Little Mermaid" (5)
12 Opposite of dry (3)
14 Scottish word for little (3)

Time ....

All The
Answers

Beginners

1

W	R	O	N	G
				I
B	E	E		F
		V		T
B	E	L	L	S

2

B	A	K	E	
I				
R			S	K	I
T				V
H	O	L	L	Y

3

N	O	S	E	
I		L		
G	L	O	V	E
H		E		
T	O	A	S	T

4

	F	I	R	
	L		O	
F	O	C	U	S
	U		N	
	R	E	D	

5

	S	K	Y	
I		I		G
C	A	N	D	Y
E		G		M
	A	S	K	

6

B	Y		D	J
O				O
O	R	G	A	N
T				A
S				H

7

	W	R	A	P
	C			O
	A	N	G	E	L
	R			E
	D	A	M	E

8

P	A	S	T	E
A		A		G
R		L	O	G
T	I	E		S
Y		S		

9

C	A	R	O	L
	L			I
F	L	I	N	G
I				H
G	U	E	S	T

10

		S		
	S	P	Y	
G		R		O
C	O	L	O	G	N	E
		U		
A	F	T	E	R

11

J	O	L	L	Y
	P		I	
F	E	A	S	T
	R		T	O
	A			Y

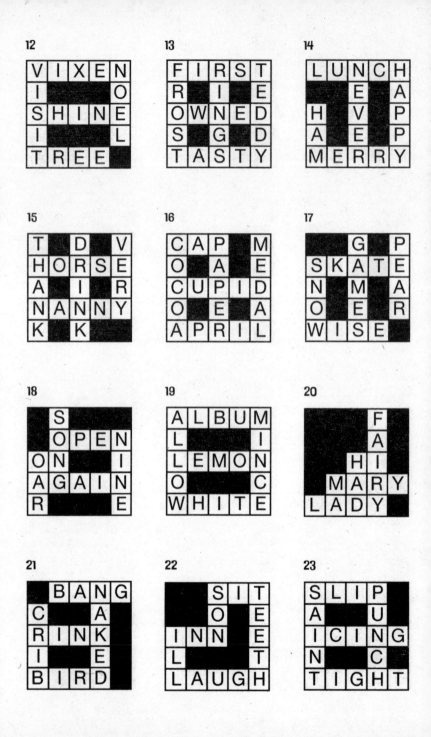

12
```
V I X E N
I     O
S H I N E
I     L
T R E E
```

13
```
F I R S T
R   I   E
O W N E D
S   G   D
T A S T Y
```

14
```
L U N C H
    E   A
H A V E P
A   E   P
M E R R Y
```

15
```
T   D   V
H O R S E
A   I   R
N A N N Y
K   K
```

16
```
C A P   M
O   A   E
C U P I D
O   E   A
A P R I L
```

17
```
    G   P
S K A T E
N   M   A
O   E   R
W I S E
```

18
```
  S
  O P E N
O N   I
A G A I N
R       E
```

19
```
A L B U M
L       I
L E M O N
O       C
W H I T E
```

20
```
      F
      A
    H I
  M A R Y
L A D Y
```

21
```
  B A N G
C   A
R I N K
I   E
B I R D
```

22
```
    S I T
    O   E
I N N   E
L       T
L A U G H
```

23
```
S L I P
A     U
I C I N G
N     C
T I G H T
```

36

```
   S   O
   C O N E
 D O   C
   F E E T
   F
```

Intermediates

37

```
        H A Y
 S A S H   N
 T     O   T
 U   C H I L L
 F     O   E
 F A T H E R
       O   S
```

38

```
 J O K E     H
 I     N     O
 N O O D L E S
 G   W O E   T
 L I S T E N
 E         K
   G H O S T S
```

39

```
 P O P C O R N
 U     E
 D A N C E R
 D         A
 I N V I T E S
 N           A
 G A R L A N D
```

40

```
 J   L
 U   U G L Y
 M   L   A
 P O L I S H
 E   A   S E E
 R I B B O N
 S   Y     S
```

41

```
   P A R C E L
   R   E   M
 H E L P   B
   S   L A R D
 D E N Y   A
 N         C
 S T A B L E
```

42

```
 C A N D L E S
 O     E     T
 M     N     O
 F O A M I E R
 O     A     I
 R     R     E
 T U R K E Y S
```

43

```
 B I B L E   J
 O   U       O
 U   S       O
 G L I M P S E
 H   E   L A P
   W R E A T H
         Y
```

44

```
 B E H A V E D
     M     E
 O G R E   L
   L   N   I
   A     T A G
   S L E I G H
   S     N O T
```

45

```
   E   F U R
 S L U R P E D
   A   I   S
 S T R E T C H
   I   N   U
 G O O D   E
   N   S O D A
```

46

```
. . J A C K .
. C L O T H .
C O . U . A .
A . . R . R .
B L O N D I E
O . . E . T .
X . . Y O Y O
```

47

```
. P E A C E .
. E . R . B .
. D O N A T E
. A . C . D .
F L O C K S .
I . . . E . .
T . M Y R R H
```

48

```
B L E S S . .
. . . . L A Y
M A S H E D .
A . L . D V D
I . I . . E .
D I C K E N S
S . T . . T .
```

49

```
. C . W I S H
C H A I N . .
. E . N U M B
B A L T I . .
. P . E T C H
D E E R . . .
. R . . . . .
```

50

```
W E L C O M E
I . I . . O .
N O N S T O P
D . E . . N .
O W N . . L .
W . . . . I .
S I L E N T .
```

51

```
. C . B U R N
. R . E . . .
. A N T . . .
S N O W M A N
H E R E . . E
O . . E . . A
P R A N C E R
```

52

```
. B . . . . .
. R . P A C K
. I . . . U .
. G I A N T .
. H . M A T .
S T A I N E D
. . . D . R .
```

53

```
C H I M N E Y
H . . . . Y .
I C I C L E S
M . D . A . E
E V E N T . R
. . . A . E V
S P L U R G E
```

54

```
T . G . . R .
R O S E T T E
U . E M U . L
M . A . M . A
P O S T B O X
E . O . L . .
T I N S E L .
```

55

```
. L E T T E R
. . . I . U .
. . L E . D .
. G L A D . O
. L A . . . L
T O M . . . P
. W A R M T H
```

56

```
. S P R U C E
. M . . . O .
P I T A . O .
. L . C A K E
R E S T . I .
I . . . O . E
P . B R A S S
```

57

```
S N A C K S .
. . . H . H .
. H O U S E .
. E . R . E .
. A C C E P T
. R . H . . U
S T Y . . . G
```

58
```
      B E A R
    B E G   A
  M A N G E R
R U D E     E
  S   A
M I T T E N S
  C   H
```

59
```
    S
F L U
U   R
M I N U T E
  D A S H E R
  M A I L
  E   N
```

60
```
D O N K E Y
E   E     U
L I E     L
I   D R I E D
V   L   D   A
E   E   E   Y
R   S W A N S
```

61
```
E N C H A N T
I           A
B   F       L
B A U B L E
L   L   U
P E E L   D
      B O W
```

62
```
  G
D A N C I N G
  B   R   R
  R   U N D O
D I E T   T
  E   C   T
  L   H A L O
```

63
```
H E L P F U L
O       U   I
L O V E D   V
I     A   G E
D I N N E R S
A     U
Y O U N G
```

64
```
S P A M     S
  I   V     P
G E C K O   E
L   H   Y   N
E M E R A L D
A   E   G
M A R K E T
```

65
```
A   T   A D D
C R O W D   E
E   W   D   E
  U N W R A P
  P     E
  O     S I X
K N I T S
```

66
```
C A R R O T S
O   O       P
S   A L O H A
Y E S   B   R
  A T T A C K
  S     M   L
  Y   C A N E
```

67
```
P
L A D L E   S
E   R   N   P
A W E S O M E
S   A   U   E
E   M A G I C
        H   H
```

68
```
S C O O P   S
    F A K E
S   A   R   A
N U M B E R S
A   U   N   O
P   S   T E N
  M E S S   S
```

69
```
G I V I N G
R   O   U   P
A D U L T   U
N   C   S   Z
D A H L     Z
    E       L
P E R F U M E
```

70

```
S E L F I E ·
E · · C · S
Q U E U E · L
U · L · B · E
I · K N E A D
N · · R · G
S N U G G L E
```

71

```
H O L M E S ·
· · E · · I
F I L L I N G
L · T · L ·
A T I S H O O
M · · A · O
E · I T I S
```

72

```
S K I J U M P
H · O · · A
A · · G E A R
R I N G · · A
I · · I C E D
N · N · · E
G O G G L E S
```

73

```
· N O S E D
A · A · · W
C O U C H · A
T · G · Y · R
I · H · M · V
O F T E N · E
N · Y · · S
```

74

```
C U I S I N E
I · R · N · X
N · O · K I P
D E N · · · R
E · · Z O N E
R · · · O · S
S E C O N D S
```

75

```
· · U · D · S
B A N Q U E T
U · I · V · I
Y · T O E · C
I · N · Y · K
N · G · · ·
G L I T T E R
```

76

```
· S C A L E S
· P · · · C
C A L M · R
· T · O · E
S U M O · E
A L A D D I N
D A D · · ·
```

77

```
E F F O R T ·
· U · R · F
· N · C · I
· F L A N · L
· A · · I · L
M I R A C L E
· R · K · R
```

78

```
· · D · · ·
· P O S T ·
F O E · · · T
· T · M U S H
N A N A · · R
· T · L · · E
· O N L I N E
```

79

```
· H O T T U B
· A · O · L
· S · A · O
· J I G S A W
W A S · T · O
· D · · · U
B E D P O S T
```

80

```
· · · T · · ·
H · · R O O F
E · · U · A
A · · L O O M
R O S Y · · I
T · I · · L
H A R M O N Y
```

81

```
C · R O B I N
A · E · U · E
L O L · S P A
L · A · Y E T
I · X · · A
N · · · · L
G L A Z E S ·
```

82

83

84

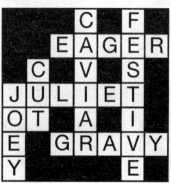

85

86

87

88

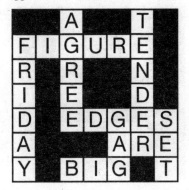

```
. . A . . T .
F I G U R E .
R . R . . N .
I . E . . D .
D . E D G E S
A . . . A R E
Y . B I G . T
```

89

```
C A M E L . .
O . U . . . H
L O S T . . O
D . I . . . O
. A C T I V E
. . A . . . E
E C L I P S E
```

90

```
S A U C E . .
N . . O . S .
O . S O C K S
W I C K . A .
C . E . . T .
A . N . . E .
P A T T E R N
```

91

```
S . . . G . .
H O G . A . .
O . E . T . Y
V . N . H . E
E . T . A . A
L . T H E I R
S L E D . . Y
```

92

```
. . . G R A N
E L S A . . .
. . . T I N Y
P U R E . . .
. . . A F A R
M E N U . . .
. . . X M A S
```

Advanced

93

Puzzle 93 grid:
- S
- E T C
- S T O V E
- A · · C · · U
- B R E A K F A S T
- K · · I · · B
- A N N I E
- A G E
- S

94

S	H	E	P	H	E	R	D	S
N		R		G				W
O		E		G	L	E	E	
W	A	N	T		N			E
F		Z		O				T
L		N	E	I	G	H		C
A	X	E	L			I	D	O
K						K		R
E	V	E	R	G	R	E	E	N

95

	C			T				
	L	O	V	I	N	G	L	Y
W	I	N		L		O		
	M	E	A	L		L		A
	B			D		D		S
W	O	N	D	E	R	F	U	L
I	N		O			I		E
G			O			S		E
	W	O	R	K	S	H	O	P

96

V	O	L	U	N	T	E	E	R
A		A		O			X	
C	A	N	N	O	N		C	
A		T		N		W	H	O
T	E	E	N		D		A	
I		R		F	U	N	N	Y
O	I	N	K		N		G	
N			I			K	N	E	E
	H	I	D	E	S			

97

F	A	N	C	Y			C	
R			U		S	L	O	W
O			T		U		N	
C	O	L	O	U	R		G	
K			U		P	R	A	M
	G	A	T	O	R			A
	N			P	I	L	O	T
G	A	L	A		S			C
	W		S	P	E	E	C	H

98

```
T O U C H I N G .
. R . M . . U .
S N O W B A L L .
. A . O X . P E
S M A R T . S . M
. E . S . . U . U
O N E H O R S E .
. T . I N . H .
. . S P E C I A L
```

99

```
D . . C Y C L E S
R . G . R . . A .
U . L O B E . G .
M . O . E T A . .
M I S T L E T O E
E . S . I . T . B
R . . F E T A . O
. W . . V . C O O
R E F R E S H . K
```

100

```
. . . . B Y .
. . . . R E .
. C A R L O A D
C A N . . R A M
. R A . . . Y .
. A M . . . T .
. M . M Y . I .
. E . P O . M .
. L E I S U R E
```

101

```
P I A N O . . C .
. . O . D R O P .
. G U . O . R .
. R G . N . D .
. E . A U N T I E
F A S T . E . A .
A T E . F R I L L
W . A . . . . L .
N A T I V I T Y .
```

102

```
F I R E P L A C E
L . E . I . R . V
I O U . C A R V E
E . N . K . I . N
S T I L L . V . .
. . O . E . E W E
D A N I S H . A .
I . . . U . . I .
P O P . E M P T Y
```

103

```
F R A G R A N C E
R . S . N . O .
E X P E C T . T .
N . . . I T S .
C R E A M . U . S
H . M . O X . P
. . L O U V R E A
. . J . I . D . R
. F I R E W O R K
```

104

```
C A R O U S E L L
R   O       A
A B B E Y   V
N   O   A W A Y
B U T T E R
E     R   T R I P
R O Y A L   O   L
R     I   A   A
Y A W N   G R I N
```

105

```
              S
M A D E   R E A L L
I       P I N   O
D I A M O N D   G
N   U   M S     C
I   R I P E N   A
G O O S E       B
H   R   I       I
T R A D I T I O N
```

106

```
  R E L I G I O N
  E   M   M   E
  M   S A F A R I
F I X   G A G   G
O X   R E L I S H
U     E   S N O B
R   S P R E E   O
T     A       U
H O L Y   D E A R
```

107

```
L   D       L
A D O     G I R L
D E C O R A T E
  C     D   C
B E L O N G   E
  M       E P I C
  B E A S T   V
  E         V E
T R U N K   O D E
```

108

```
R E J O I C E   K
    U   H   E
  T O T   E N V Y
  H A L L S   S
W O K E   T   B
  U   T E N D E R
A G E S   U   A
  H       T I M E
  T W I G S   S
```

109

```
C   S   R U S T Y
H E L P S   A
O   A   P A L   H
C E L E B R A T E
O   O   C D   A
L A M P   H   P
A   O       M
T O B O G G A N
E   R       N
```

110

```
S T I R . . . . C
. E . . . F . H
P A R K . O . R
I M . . . L . I
E . P E C K I S H
R . R . . L . T A
C R I M S O N . N
E . Z . . R . D
. N E W Y E A R .
```

111

```
B A N D S . . . A
O . E . . F U N
A M A Z E S . . O
R . R . T . . R
D I S P L A Y . A
G . . . . N E C K
A D O R E D . A
M . R . . . . B
E X C I T E D
```

112

```
P R A Y E R S .
L . R . V . A X E
E M O T I O N . G
N . M . T . D I G
T R A V E L . . C
Y . A . I . . U
. K . L A P T O P
. O . U . S . F .
G I V E . . U F O
```

113

```
. D R E S S I N G
. A . H . R . R
T W I N E . O . E
I . S I L E N C E
G R I L L . M . T
H . N . . T A X I
T . . M O A N . N
S . . O . P . . G
. . P I E C E S
```

114

```
B O R E D O M .
. U . . . K A L E
. R . C . G . .
. S T U F F I N G
. . O B E . C . I
E N T E R T A I N
. . T . R . L . G
P O E T I C . . E
. . R . S O L A R
```

115

```
H A I L S T O R M
U . . . E . . . A
B A T H T U B . R
. . B . . . A . V
C H A R M . N . E
. . . U . . G . L
C U P . N . E . L
. . A . C . R . E
P U R C H A S E D
```

116

```
U N I V E R S A L
P . . . . . P . U
B E E F . J I N X
E . R . . R . U .
A H E A D . I . R
T . Q U I E T L Y
. N U D E . . O .
. A . . . . . G .
. L E A V E S . .
```

117

```
C O A T . . . . G
R . . H O S E . R
A C H E . T U B E
S . R . U . O W .
H O G M A N A Y .
. . A . N . . . .
. . L . I . . . .
. . . . N . . . .
A L L E R G Y . .
```

118

```
D O O R K N O B .
O . . . . . . A .
L O A F . G A L E
L . . R . . L . .
. . B R O T H E R
M . A . O . T . .
S . L A M B . . .
S I L K . . . . .
K . . A P P E A L
```

119

```
F R U I T C A K E
I . N . R . R . .
V I B R A N T . .
E . O . F . I C Y
. D R I F T S . O
B I N . I . T . N
. N . . C H I L D
. E . . . . C . E
G R E E N . . . R
```

120

```
W . . . . . K . .
I . I . . D I S H
F E L T . . N . E
E . L . M A G M A
. . U . A . . U V
P . S C R O O G E
U N I . B . O . N
S . O . L . Z . L
S I N C E R E L Y
```

121

```
B E L L Y . F I B
E . Y . A . L . R
T W I N K L E . I
H . N . . E X A M
L E G E N D . . .
E . . L . G A S P
H U M B L E . . O
E . . O . . . . U
M . W A L N U T .
```

122

```
A S T R A Y   T
  H   E   F A R
S O C C E R   I
  P   I   A   K
  P A T I E N C E
  E   A   N
B R I L L I A N T
A               V
G E N E R O U S
```

123

```
  F R E E Z I N G
  O   X   E     L
B L O C K S     O
  L   E   T O M B
W O O L     N   A
W I L T     E   L
  L E O     S
  S N O W I N G
    T       E
```

124

```
B R U N C H
        O         T
        U     R   O
D I C E S   H     G
O       D I L U T E
V E G A N   B     T
E D   M   C A S H
    E       R     E
  N O V E M B E R
```

125

```
  B L A Z E   R
  A         B I B
R A P   T   S
E   O   R O B E S
S   R   I       A
P U T O F F     U
E   I   L A W   C
C O O P E R A T E
T   N   M G   R
```

126

```
A P P E T I T E
D I Y         A
V   J E S T E R
E   A   L   L
R O M C O M   Y
T R A M P   Y
S I S   P R O U D
  O     Y   L
  N     Y   K
```

127

```
M O V I N G     C
        R O T A A
T R A M   A     M
  E   O A T H   E
  C L O S E D   R
H O P   S     F A
  V   P I P E R S
  E     S     E
C R E A T E   E
```

128

129

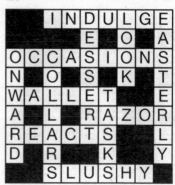

130

131

132

133

134

C	H	I	C	K	S		
	O		O		E	N	D	S
	T	R	U	S	T			P
	R			T	A	I	L	
S	W	I	S	S				E
W		N	E	W	B	O	R	N
A		L		E		L		D
P	E	A	R	L		A		I
	W	E	L	L	F	E	D	

135

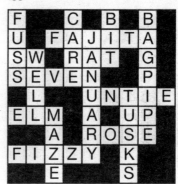

F		C		B		B	
U		F	A	J	I	T	A
S	W		R	A	T		G
S	E	V	E	N			P
	L			U	N	T	I	E
E	L	M		A		U	P
	A		R	O	S	E
F	I	Z	Z	Y		K
	E					S

136

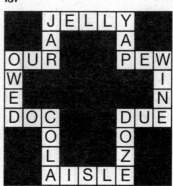

A		C	U	S	T	A	R	D
F		A		L		R		U
F	O	R	G	I	V	E		T
E		E		D	I	A	R	Y
C	O	F	F	E	E		E	
T		U		S	W	E	E	P
I	D	L	E				L	
O								
N	A	R	R	A	T	O	R	

137

J	E	L	L	Y
	A			A
O	U	R			P	E	W
W							I
E							N
D	O	C			D	U	E
	O				O		
	L				Z		
A	I	S	L	E

138

	R		D	A	W	N	
H	E	R	O	D			B
	L		U		G		L
	I		B	A	N	A	N	A
	T	U	T	U		L		N
T			T		L	L		K
O			T	H	R	O	N	E
T			O		P	E	T
O	F	F	E	R			W

139

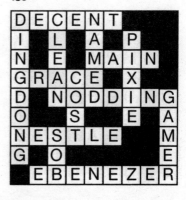

D	E	C	E	N	T	
I		L		A		P
N		E		M	A	I	N
G	R	A	C	E		X
D		N	O	D	D	I	N	G
O			S		E		A
N	E	S	T	L	E		M
G		O					E
	E	B	E	N	E	Z	E	R

140

```
S . B . F . . .
H E R A L D
I . O . E I G H T
F R O Z E N . A
T A C . C . . M
. C H I E F . P
J K . . . A . E
R E M E M B E R
. T
```

141

```
. . . S H O W
. P A N . . E
. E . E . D E W
I N F A N T . . E
. G . K . A . B
C U R I O U S . B
. I . N . R . E
N . . B U I L D
. G O E S
```

142

```
G E N T L E M E N
L . O . I . E . E
A D O P T . E . V
M . K . T I T L E
O . . L . . . . R
U N C L E . L . L
R . H . . C O M A
. . E . . . N . N
. . F R I N G E D
```

143

```
. F L U F F Y . B
. A . N . . O . U
. V . D . O D D S
T O K E N . E . .
. U . R . F L I P
. R . . . E . . E
A I R P O R T . T
. T . A . R . . A
M E O W . Y E L L
```

144

```
T U C K E D I N .
. N O I S E . . K
C O M P A N I O N
O . M . T . . . O
N . O . P . H U T
T O T A L L Y . .
E . I . A . P A T
N . O . I . E . .
T . N A T U R A L
```

Ace Puzzlers

145

				F	L	A	S	K	
G	I	G	G	L	E		L		
		O		W		L			B
C	H	E	W	Y		G	O		E
O		N		M	O	S	S		A
M		S	M	O	O	T	H		U
I		C		R		O			T
C	O	O	K	I	N	G			I
	U			I		W	O	L	F
	G			N		I	F		U
T	H	O	U	G	H	T	F	U	L

146

	D		C		P			
	U		H	O	T		E	
P	O	T		M		C	A	R
		H	O	B	B	Y		
	B		E		G		M	
F	L	E	A			N	I	P	S
	T		T		E		H	
		R	I	G	H	T		
A	P	E		E		S	H	Y
	A		I	M	P		E	
	D			S			M	

147

S	L	Y		C	O	N	I	F	E	R
Y		T		O		R		U	
R	E	T	R	O		A	L	O	N	G
U		I		H		T		T		B
P	S		N		C		T	H	E	Y
	T	A	K	E	A	W	A	Y		
	A		E		T		P		C	
S	M	O	T	H	E	R		C	U	E
A	P	P		R		M	A	T		
F		E	N	V	E	L	O	P	E	
E		N			R			E	

148

B	A	K	I	N	G			
A				O	C	E	A	N	S
B	A	H		A		P		
Y		E		S	L	E	E	P	S
S	P	L	I	T			R	U	G
I		L		E		D	E	M	O
T	H	O	M	A	S		C		B
	U		M	A	R	T	I	A	L
S	T	E	W		L		A		I
C				T	A	R	T	A	N
C	H	E	E	K	Y			E

149

	S			F				
	H		F	A	B	R	I	C
S	A	L	M	O	N			H
	K		U		A	F	T	E	R
D	E	P	A	R	T		I		D
I			R		R		D	
S	T		C	I	N	E	M	A	S
T	O	S	S		U		W	O	R	N
U	N		P	O	M	P	O	M		O
R		U		P		O			R
B	E	A	D		H	U	D	D	L	E

150

151

152

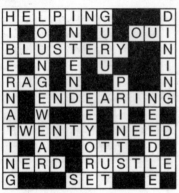

153